2-9-60

MODERN BIRD STUDY

LONDON: GEOFFREY CUMBERLEGE

OXFORD UNIVERSITY PRESS

GANNET ALIGHTING

Bonaventure Island, Quebec

Modern Bird Study

By
LUDLOW GRISCOM

Cambridge, Massachusetts
HARVARD UNIVERSITY PRESS
1947

PREFACE

THIS BOOK is the outgrowth of a series of eight lectures given at the Lowell Institute in January, 1944. They have been thoroughly revised and extended into ten chapters.

Ornithology is now so vast a subject that many topics have become separate fields of research, requiring special training or techniques. Anatomy, physiology, the contributions of bird banding, life history studies, modern experimental work in behavior and homing instincts, and other equally important phases of ornithology are here omitted, as they require separate courses of lectures or a series of chapters in a book. Those selected are the ones the author has specially studied or about which he has learned something in thirty-five years of active and extended field experience.

The first five chapters will appeal to any layman with a general interest in birds. The chapters on distribution and classification are more technical, and some knowledge of North American birds must be taken for granted. These two sciences are particularly bothersome and puzzling to amateur bird watchers, and the lectures were originally prepared at the suggestion of large numbers of friends. No similar attempt has been made to expound both the difficulties and the fascinating problems of great biological importance in both disciplines.

The main object of the book, however, is to show that the study of birds is not only a branch of scientific research, which need not be a narrow specialty, but that it also contains many topics of interest to the layman, and that the growing army of bird watchers have and can really assist the ornithologist in solving problem after problem by controlled, careful, and thorough observation.

The author greatly appreciates the opportunity to select illustrations from the fine photograph library of the National Audubon Society. Thanks and acknowledgments are due to the D. Appleton-Century Co., New York, for permission to reproduce three migration route maps from F. M. Chapman's Handbook to the Birds of Eastern North America, and also to the American Museum of Natural History, New York, for the privilege of reproducing three faunal maps from F. M. Chapman's Distribution of Bird-Life in Ecuador, *Bulletin*, vol. 55, 1926.

L. G.

Cambridge, Massachusetts
January, 1945

CONTENTS

CONTENTS

ILLUSTRATIONS

MAPS AND DIAGRAMS

MODERN BIRD STUDY

CHAPTER I

DEVELOPMENT OF FIELD ORNITHOLOGY

ORNITHOLOGY may be simply defined as the scientific study of birds, consisting in the effort to solve problems about birds and to find out new facts about them. Before one can readily understand certain modern developments, a brief historical summary may be helpful. In ancient and medieval times such interest as there was in birds was largely a question of their use to man in various ways—for food, game, or sport, or, especially in ancient times with vultures, eagles, and owls, for augury and omens. It now seems surprising how slowly the idea arose that birds were pretty, had attractive songs, and were worth watching and having around for their own sakes.

The ancient Greeks had very few names for small song birds. One noun τρικκος (*trikkos*) was a general term for any small bird, and might have been used for nearly one hundred species. This is in marked contrast with certain primitive peoples like the Hawaiians, who had a special name for each of the great majority of their small landbirds, as well as the larger and more striking ones.

In Europe, as a matter of fact, a knowledge of birds lagged way behind that of plants and flowers, as the incentive of the old herbalists was lacking. This incentive was the belief that all plants were of some medicinal benefit to man, if only he could find out what it was. As a result, there were many books, with beautiful illustrations, on the flowering plants of Europe many decades before any careful work of the sort was produced with regard to birds.

In the middle of the eighteenth century a Swedish naturalist by the name of Linnaeus invented a scientific system of classification. Every living thing, whether plant or animal, was given two Latin names, a species name and a genus name, and all living things were grouped in "families" and "orders" according to the supposed degree of their relationships. The bird world in those days was a very simple one indeed. There were only six or seven orders and very few families, and great numbers of birds were put in the genus of the thrushes or the warblers or the finches or the buntings. At any rate, the Linnaean system of classification prevails to this day, and has been universally adopted by naturalists throughout the world.

The invention of this system, the founding of the first natural history museums, and the rapid expansion of the colonial empires of the leading nations ushered in what in the history of ornithology may be called the period of exploration. People realized that there was a great and previously unsuspected variety of birds, and those interested set out to discover, describe, and classify them. At the start, they did not hesitate to write books on the birds of the entire world. Then, they specialized in continents, and finally they got down to countries or political subdivisions. The first list of Massachusetts birds was published about a century ago, and about 1900 the first county lists of birds began to appear.

About 1900, William Brewster, a noted ornithologist of Cambridge, Massachusetts, wrote a book on "The Birds of the Cambridge Region," which included not only the present city of Cambridge, but also the towns of Belmont, Arlington, and parts, at least, of Lincoln, Waltham, and Watertown. At the present moment, the "Cambridge Region" of Brewster is being subdivided among the birds of Mount Auburn Cemetery in Cambridge, the birds of Belmont, the birds of Waltham, etc. The increasingly fine subdivision of the units should be noted.

As regards the birds themselves, orders and families multiplied, and it is now some time since anyone has lived long enough to list competently all the birds of the world known at the present moment. Great complications have arisen, some of fundamental biological interest, which will be the subject of a later chapter.

By way of summary, however, it may be pointed out that ornithology became primarily concerned with classification and exploration. As late as 1901, Robert Ridgway, then the dean of American ornithologists, defined scientific ornithology as the identification and classification of birds, and he defined field ornithology as the collecting and stuffing of specimens. We have by no means fully recovered from this preposterously narrow definition. But when I was a boy the serious young student of birds was expected to shoot or collect his quota of local robins, phoebes, and warblers. To be identified, the dead bird had to be in hand. The bird book of the day was highly technical and, in part, an anatomical treatise; there was a detailed description of the bird, a statement of its range or distribution, a description of the nest and eggs, if known, with measurements; and a brief statement about "habits." You then passed on to the next bird!

Nine-tenths of the problems concerning birds which today are the subjects for research and study were not even hinted at in the textbooks of my youth. The same young student looked forward to the day when he, too, could go with a museum exploring expedition (called by one of my colleagues at Harvard "a high-class plundering expedition"), to some out-of-the-way corner of the earth and discover some bird new to science.

Now, I am old enough to have been brought up under this system. Incidentally, my colleague's witty remark was an idea which was shared by some of the governing officials of the remote countries visited. I well remember arriving in Panama on one occasion a good many years ago. I, of course, had to apply to the authorities for a permit to bring in arms, guns, and ammunition, and to use those weapons in the country. I cooled my heels around Panama City day after day, waiting for these permits to come in. They never did. But one fine morning a most beautiful youth in a magnificent uniform called on me with the greatest ceremony at my hotel. He presented the compliments of the President of Panama, who wished to know if I could possibly find it convenient to wait upon him at eleven o'clock that morning. I most certainly was able to find it convenient to do so, and, when I was received and ushered into audience with him, I found that the Cabinet had met in executive session at nine o'clock that morning and had passed an act founding the Natural History Museum of Panama. This act required that hereafter all collecting expeditions for foreign museums should deposit a duplicate series of the birds or the animals that they obtained in the Natural History Museum of Panama.

This proviso is now a common one, first started, I believe, by the great Gizeh museum at Cairo. In some other countries it is practically impossible for outsiders to secure collecting permits. In most countries collecting permits are strictly limited; certain birds and mammals are specially protected, and the number of specimens of each species to be taken is also limited. These precautions are largely due to two obvious factors. In many cases of our better-known North American birds, enough specimens for scientific purposes already exist. The small, recently founded museums can secure the needed specimens by purchase or exchange, or can borrow them for some special study. I regret to have to state that some modern restrictions are in part caused by the misconduct of professional collectors in the past, who violated the laws of the country, or the terms of their permit, or behaved in a hopelessly tactless manner—shooting on private property, for instance, without permission. One famous collector of fresh-water fishes in South America used to dynamite the rivers as the easiest way of collecting in quantity. When the outraged authorities hastened to repair a gap in the law, and made it illegal, this collector kept right on dynamiting the rivers, as he could well afford to pay the fines! Not all museum expeditions have even been "high-class" plundering expeditions.

However this may be, in the course of the development of the exploring age various misconceptions about birds arose, since the "specimen" was the proof of everything, and ninety per cent of the possible facts of interest about the bird disappeared with its death. One of these misconceptions was the status of the species, whether abundant, common, or rare. Psychologically, an amusing situation developed in this connection. Great differences in point of view arose between the exploring or cabinet naturalist and the local student. The museum man, upon receiving the tenth known specimen of record of some rare bird from South American jungles, would begin to feel it was getting to be pretty well known, whereas the student of birds in the United States who read of some bird, one of the very few remaining ones known from only ten specimens, would think that that particular bird presented a most fascinating problem challenging solution, and he would bend every effort to find out as much about it as he could.

I well remember my first exploring expedition. It happened to be to the Central American Republic of Nicaragua. I was assistant to my late colleague, Waldron deW. Miller. Before going, we made most unusual preparations. We drew up a list of all the birds that had ever been recorded from Nicaragua, and on this list we made up a sort of a rough field key, by which all these strange tropical birds could be recognized, should we come across them in the country. We made up a second list, a highly special list, of the great rarities which were only known from one or two specimens of record, which we were to make every possible effort to find. One of these great rarities, I remember very well, was a species of cactus wren known as the rufous-necked cactus wren (*Heleodytes rufinucha*). We were very much surprised and a little "let down" when it turned out to be one of the five or six commonest birds of the country, in the relatively arid scrub of the interior.

We had with us the professional who had made the only previous collections of birds from Nicaragua, and we asked him how it came about that he had sent only one specimen of this particular cactus wren back to the United States. He answered: "Why, you people have always told me that my job depended upon getting the rare birds, so, of course, I never bothered with any of the common ones!"

I cite this story merely to show how one can be misled as to the real facts, solely on the basis of specimens of the bird in a museum.

A quarter of a century ago, I remember looking at the collection of a noted amateur egg collector in the States. At that time he had one of the largest and the most complete collections of eggs in existence. Somewhat to my surprise, I found that he had 235 sets of eggs of the robin. There was every possible type of variation shown in this series. There were sets of three eggs, four eggs, five eggs, and six eggs. There were small eggs, medium-sized eggs, and large eggs, and there were pale blue eggs, medium-colored blue eggs, and dark blue eggs; but, when every possible allowance for all these variations had been made, there were still 150 sets or so of just robins' eggs. When I asked him why there were so many, he said: "That proves that the robin is the commonest nesting bird in this part of the country!"

Well, as a matter of fact, we knew that already! But, my story will serve to introduce certain phases of modern field ornithology which deal with observations of the living bird and with problems where the bird must be alive, not dead, to be solved. Some of these problems are dealt with in later chapters under the headings of distribution, migration, intelligence, adaptability, and various other topics.

The fundamental necessity was the development of a technique of correctly identifying living birds, without which this type of modern field ornithology would be impossible. I shall say very little here about that technique. Techniques are mastered, as all very well know, through a natural aptitude fostered by long practice and study. Nobody ever learned to play the piano by reading books on how to play the piano, and nobody ever learned how to identify birds in the field by reading, or listening to me or anyone else tell how it is done. Suffice it here to say that the development of this technique has made prodigious strides in the last three decades, and what people are now able to do in the way of instantly recognizing a large number of birds by song, notes, tricks of flight, shape, etc., entirely apart from their colors, seems perfectly fabulous to the uninitiated and was flatly declared to be impossible a generation ago.

Indeed, we now know that there are very few cases of two similar species of North American birds which cannot be told apart, granted favorable conditions of observation. When it comes to subspecies, or geographic races, this situation is reversed; very few of them can be positively identified in life, and the collecting gun is absolutely essential in certain special fields of research.

I well remember a noted ornithologist in an eastern city, belonging very definitely to the older generation, who was the guardian angel and father to a very active bird club whose members were largely students at a near-by college. Several of these members subsequently became ornithologists of note themselves. In the course of the spring migration these young men would get out early in the morning, and they would then report the arrival of various warblers and other birds from the south. Their president became more and more disturbed, because he felt that his club was beginning to run away with him. He knew perfectly well that not a single one of these young men owned a gun, so how did they know what all these warblers were in the tops of the trees? They said that they were able to tell them by various minute differences in size, shape, tricks of flight, and in addition by their brilliant and well-known color patterns. He was entirely unable to do anything of the sort himself, but being an honest gentleman, he decided to look into it and give it a try. So he went out one May morning with his gun into the woods and waited until a flock of warblers came along. The young members of the club would tell him what a particular warbler was in the top of a tree, and he would shoot it down. To his astonishment it turned out to be just the warbler these young men said it was! So he decided that maybe there was something in the modern technique of sight identification after all.

As a matter of fact, to be fair to the older generation, it was almost impossible in their day; they did not have any prism glasses; there were no colored plates; there were no guides giving in the text all the points which people could look for and use in living birds—all of which we now take for granted. The only substitutes for all these aids and easements were long years of experience and a specially detailed knowledge of birds, which was most certainly gained by handling specimens, a type of knowledge which the average amateur, alas! no longer possesses.

The development of this technique and its mastery by an increasing number of people have caused the development of various hobbies in the way of bird study by people whom I am forced to allude to as amateurs, thanks to the defects of the English language, merely because they do not spend their entire time at it, and are not paid for ornithological research. There are all kinds of enjoyable outdoor bird sports and games which have developed today, and thousands of people throughout the United States are now going out and looking for birds on one ground of interest or another and are having an exceedingly good time. I might add that a very substantial percentage of them are most certainly coöperating with ornithologists, and their observations are definitely contributing to our knowledge of birds. Many of these games, however, while thoroughly enjoyable—and I have played them all myself and I yield to none in my enjoyment of them—must not be confused with the use of the technique of field identification in ornithological research.

To sum up again, there was one type of field ornithology with the exploring and collecting age and there is another type today. But the modern technique of field ornithology, with modern problems, did not and could not arise in any region until the exploring age was virtually over in that particular part of the world, and the collection of further specimens was superfluous. Just as 235 sets of robins' eggs are unnecessary to establish the abundance of the robin, so is it unnecessary to shoot large numbers of terns every fall to determine the relative abundance of four possible species in this state. Similarly, we do not shoot all the sparrows every year to tell them apart. How absurd it would be with Mrs. Nice's great Song Sparrow Life History if she had had to collect every song sparrow she had observed or studied as a voucher for the correctness of her identification, or if she had not been able to tell the sparrows apart without collecting them, and if the results of her Life History were impugned and falsified by the occasional admixture of some wrong kind of sparrow in her results!

The battle for sight records and field identification of the living bird has been won, so far as I know, and there is no real quarrel left about what birds can be recognized alive and when this recognition can be used in scientific research.

The only problem left is over the confusion of the two techniques. It is the modern school which is constantly sinning in this direction. They insist on trying to apply their newly gained technique in parts of the world or in cases where the exploring age is not yet over, and this is where they have the science of ornithology really worried.

A rather pathetic illustration of this came to my attention a year or so ago, in connection with an amateur bird student in southern Texas. I have been out in the field with him, and I regard him as one of the most naturally gifted and expert men in the field that I have ever known in the United States. Over a period of ten years he studied intensively the birds of his section of southern Texas, until he had found all the possible species, until he knew the status of each one of them with a reasonable degree of perfection, and then he looked about for new fields to conquer. Just to the south of him was the vast Republic of Mexico. He had never seen a specimen of a Mexican bird. He had no books. There were no guides or colored plates in existence. He had no knowledge of the literature, and, sentimentally—for which weakness I do not blame him—he was absolutely unwilling to shoot birds. He undoubtedly had many golden opportunities. It just so happens that the moment you cross the Mexican border you get back into the exploring stage. Our knowledge of the birds of Mexico is merely on the surface. New birds are being discovered there nearly every month. We know little or nothing about their habits, their nests and eggs; and, in innumerable cases, the range of any bird in Mexico will be found to extend farther east, north, west, or south than we now suppose.

There was, undoubtedly, any amount of opportunity for this particular amateur to add to knowledge. His ideas of what some of the birds were that he saw were at times incorrect, but in other cases, unquestionably, he was right. The question arises, how are we to tell which observations to credit? Which of his facts and discoveries do the editors of the scientific journals publish, and which do they reject? As a matter of fact, there is no possible criterion by which they can decide which ones are correct and which ones are possibly in error, and the only thing they can do is to publish none of them for lack of final and absolute proof.

In the New England States, however, the exploring stage is practically over. Collecting a specimen for scientific record is necessary only with certain highly technical subspecies, or in the case of some accidental straggler from so remote and unexpected a region that a voucher in some official New England or state museum is desirable as proof, rather than the testimony of the observer.

As an incident to prove this point, it seems only fair that, instead of picking upon some amateur, I should tell a story on myself. We have here in the eastern states two well-known woodpeckers, the hairy and the downy. The chief difference between them is that the hairy woodpecker is a larger edition of the downy woodpecker. Now, it so happens that both these woodpeckers range from tree line in northwestern Alaska, south to California and Florida, and, as with a great many other birds having such a wide latitudinal range, we find that the largest birds are in the far north and that size steadily decreases southward.

Here in Massachusetts we occasionally get winter visitations of larger subspecies of both hairy and downy woodpeckers from more northern and northwestern sections, and, as they differ from their relatives here in Massachusetts only by being larger, we get the following confusing and difficult question of size. The degree of difference between the largest Massachusetts downy and the smallest Massachusetts hairy is less than the degree of difference between the smallest Massachusetts hairy and the largest northern hairy woodpecker. And the degree of difference between the largest northwestern Nelson's downy woodpecker and a small Massachusetts downy is almost as great as is the degree of difference between some local downies and hairies.

Two or three years ago some friends and I happened to notice a woodpecker pitch into a tree near us, and we thought at first it was a hairy woodpecker. After looking at it carefully, we decided that it was too small, and that it must be a downy woodpecker. But we had a distinct impression that if it was a downy woodpecker, it certainly was a very large one indeed. So I shot the bird and it turned out to be a typical specimen of the northwestern Nelson's downy woodpecker, which is a straggler in Massachusetts in winter, and an interesting addition to our museum collection.

In publishing and announcing this particular record, we found that it was the first time that Nelson's downy woodpecker had been reported as occurring in New England. No textbook on New England birds happens to mention this larger subspecies, and the local bird students had never heard of it, and they knew nothing about it. Being presented in this way with positive proof that a Nelson's downy woodpecker could be recognized in life, they began to keep their eyes open for very large downy woodpeckers in winter, and, on one occasion and another one observer or another in this state in the last two or three years has felt pretty sure that he has found one. But, without any gun or permit to collect, the record has never been positively substantiated.

Well, I, too, have been keeping my eye out for a second Nelson's downy woodpecker. Mr. Oscar Root and I found one last December just after we had been seeing other hairy and downy woodpeckers. I collected that particular specimen, also, and was quite pleased about it. I reported it to a group of friends that evening. It was a cold winter's night and I got home late. I was tired, so I left the unfortunate woodpecker in the rear of my car where it could freeze nicely. The next morning on my way to the Museum I opened the back of my car, and when I took the woodpecker out the scales fell off my eyes, and it looked for all the world like nothing but a hairy woodpecker to me. Upon carefully measuring it, I found it to be just a hairy woodpecker. My great mistake was that the bird that I saw and shot was indeed smaller than the hairy woodpeckers which I had been seeing, but I shot the wrong bird. I should have shot the big hairy woodpecker that I had just seen, and not the small one I last saw. This is a case in which the exploring age has not ended in Massachusetts, and this story should serve as a warning to people who think that critical subspecies can be identified in life.

As a good illustration of a contribution by field ornithology to science, I now revert to my remarks on an earlier page on the status of the species. The old books called birds abundant, common, uncommon, rare, or occasional. In no one direction has modern field ornithology produced a greater advance of knowledge, without collecting a single specimen. Psychologically, it turned out that from the observer's or the recorder's standpoint, birds were rarer when he was a beginner, and they became commoner as he became more experienced. The second point that developed was that no two observers used these general terms alike. The result was that the olive-backed thrush was reported as a common migrant around New York City and around Boston, but it proved to be five to ten times more numerous around New York than around Boston. The Blackburnian warbler, universally reported as a common transient throughout the Atlantic seaboard, is actually common only in the Ohio Valley, and is always relatively uncommon elsewhere. With scientific observation, it transpired that the numbers of no bird remained the same two years in succession and that many were subject to marked oscillations of abundance, all camouflaged under general terms.

The modern criteria of abundance, therefore, are based on a continental scale, never the estimate of a purely local experience. Counts of individuals per season, per trip, or per year are made with every species of bird, and in a great many cases counts of individuals per day or per hour or per mile turn out to be worth while.

Since I am not mathematically minded, it happens to mean very little to me when I read a report which says of a certain bird that it averages 355 ten thousandths of a bird per trip. But that happens to be my particular defect. I am naturally poor at figures, and to those who have no such handicap that particular method of describing the status of birds is probably perfectly permissible. But there is no agreement as yet as to the proper or ideal method of making bird counts and assuring the fact that A's observations will be fairly comparable with those of B; this is still a matter of research and it is in the experimental stage.

Birds turn out to be so variable that no method of counting will possibly work equally well for all of them. There are most elaborate and difficult questions of habitat factors, for instance. If there is only one marsh in the desert valleys of southern California, all the ducks in that part of North America will go to that marsh, and one can see fabulous numbers of ducks. There is a recent record of a million and a third pintail ducks in one such marsh in one day. Nobody can see a million robins in a lifetime of field experience in Massachusetts, but does that prove that there are more pintail ducks than robins?

It should be apparent that in many of these remarks

bird counting serves merely to give us much greater precision in evaluating their relative abundance than the vague general terms in use a generation ago. Marked oscillation in abundance of one species over a period of years is something much more important, and may lead to far-reaching studies of its life history. The subject is worthy of some elaboration here.

In the first place, some competent and continuous observation is obviously required before any increase or decrease of a given bird can even be suspected. The matter is then called to the attention of observers, and a great many people over a wide area join in a special study, and we here assume that a change in status is proved. The question then arises—what are the causes or factors concerned? This question can as yet be answered definitely only in a minority of cases. With the ruffed grouse, for instance, this popular game bird seems to have cycles of prosperity of about eleven years. Starting from a low point which lasts several years, a sudden boom takes place; several good years result in a great increase in the population; disease then breaks out and the total number is rapidly cut down to the original low point, which marks the beginning of the new cycle. Curiously enough, hunting has been proved to make no difference, which merely means that this cyclic ebb and flow of population goes on just the same in the unhunted wilderness and the controlled game preserve. We can be even more precise, and state that the grouse is divided into innumerable minor "populations," each of which pursues its natural cycle on a different timetable, without any correspondence between adjacent populations. Thus near Boston the grouse of Essex County, of the central uplands of Massachusetts, of southeastern and of west central New Hampshire are four separate "populations."

Much greater difficulty was experienced with certain fresh-water ducks, which decreased rapidly some years ago. As they ranged widely over the whole continent, the decrease was hard to prove, and was hotly disputed by some sportsmen at first, who claimed they had seen "plenty" and resented restricted shooting privileges. Here the primary cause proved to be the great reduction in the breeding ranges due to civilization and agriculture; a purely secondary cause was shooting; the depleted stock of survivors could not stand the old-fashioned open season from September 15 to January 10.

A sudden failure of a primary food supply can cause disaster. Thus the eel-grass blight on the Atlantic seaboard reduced the brant by ninety per cent in two years. The survivors learned just in time to find other food which gave them adequate nourishment.

Marked variations in number are now well known in many birds at the extreme northern or southern limits of their range, where they are local, uncommon, or rare. These are what are called "overflow" populations, and exist only in a series of "good" years when individuals are crowded out of the normal range by competition and overpopulation. In other cases the extreme periphery of the range is a question of climatic tolerance. Thus the Carolina wren is constantly spreading north into New England, only to be killed—not, as it happens, by severe cold, but by heavy snow which buries the fallen logs and brush-piles among which it finds its food.

Finally there is a series of cases where birds have increased or decreased for no apparent reason. To the scientist these are much more interesting than changes having perfectly obvious causes, such as persecution or destruction of habitat. The cardinal and tufted titmouse, always two very common birds, are now steadily pushing northward. We have no idea why; nor do we know why they didn't do it many decades ago, since the movement is apparently entirely successful. In my youth the yellow-throated vireo was a common summer bird from New York north to Boston; it was partially domesticated, nesting in parks and orchards, in village shade trees, and along the banks of streams and rivers. Conditions have remained the same, but the vireo began fading out rapidly from 1917 on, and is now rare and local. We do not know why.

There are consequently excellent and useful reasons for counting birds as carefully as possible. The observer who just checks his day's list on a printed card is wasting a good opportunity.

REFERENCES

1. GRISCOM, LUDLOW. Problems of Field Identification. *Auk*, vol. 39, no. 1, January 1922, pp. 31–41.
2. GRISCOM, LUDLOW. Changes in the Status of Certain Birds in the New York City Region. *Auk*, vol. 46, no. 1, January 1929, pp. 45–57.

3. GRISCOM, LUDLOW. Modern Problems in Field Identification. *Bird-Lore*, vol. 38, February 1936, pp. 12–18.
4. GRISCOM, LUDLOW. Decrease and Increase of Massachusetts Birds. *Bulletin of the Massachusetts Audubon Society*, vol. 22, no. 3, April 1938, pp. 10–14.
5. HICKEY, JOSEPH J. *A Guide to Bird Watching*. New York: Oxford University Press, 1943. 8vo, xiv + 265 pp.

CHAPTER II

CAPACITY AND INTELLIGENCE OF BIRDS

THE subject of behavior and intelligence in birds is a little known and highly disputatious one. Any discussion of it must be prefaced with the caution that birds are a separate class of vertebrates, sharply distinct from mammals; that they are composed of many different orders and families; and that many of them are of more primitive structure and far older origin in geological time than the modern, small song and perching birds, which are the dominant group today. All remarks in this chapter will refer to the last group, unless it is specifically mentioned to the contrary.

It is almost impossible to avoid comparing birds with mankind, whose behavior and intelligence is not only a source of constant study and research, but often of keen anxiety. But any serious effort at comparison is positively absurd. To endow birds with "human" traits, as is popularly done, is tantamount to implying as a premise that 18,000 species of one class of vertebrates can really bear comparison with the most remarkably evolved species of a higher class. For this reason really scientific studies of bird behavior carefully avoid the use of terms and nouns used to denote human traits; they employ a special terminology

which often sounds absurd in one direction, or is mean-
ingless to the layman in another.

To develop this theme a little further, science advances
by proof. If we are in doubt whether A is afraid or not,
he can often settle the question by telling us that he is
indeed "scared to death," in addition to showing the usual
signs and symptoms. The emotion of fear in birds is *inferred*
by their behavior, and long-continued observation raises
this inference to the plane of overwhelming conviction,
but it can scarcely be *proved*, like a proposition in geome-
try. If you wished to investigate my sense of smell, how
handicapped you would be if it was understood that I
could never answer any questions, would never tell whether
I smelled something or not, whether the smell was strong
or faint, pleasant or unpleasant.

It would appear that birds have very rudimentary senses
of smell, taste, and touch, but that they are immeasurably
our superiors in their powers of hearing and sight. They
possess very high normal body temperatures, ranging from
103 to 112 degrees Fahrenheit. They have a normal pulse
rate which is nearly double that of human beings, and they
are, consequently, perfectly adapted to withstand extremes
of both heat and cold.

One's outstanding impression of birds is that they are
bursting with energy. Intense activity, constant alertness,
extreme restlessness, are characteristic of birds, and they
seem to require astonishingly little sleep and rest.

Years ago, in the spring migration in May, it was my
custom to arrive at a certain field in New Jersey before

dawn. I had a half-mile walk up a railroad track to some woods, which I planned to reach at daybreak. As I walked up this railroad track in the early morning, I could hear the calls and chirps of the migrating birds overhead, and as dawn arrived and daylight broke, these chirps and calls would come from a lower and lower altitude, and, finally, I would be able to make out the little forms flying north, a relatively few feet overhead. On one occasion a small warbler flew down into a little maple tree on the edge of the track, and, as a matter of interest, I stayed there and watched what it did. It kept perfectly still for twenty minutes, and for part of this time it had its head under its wing. It was obviously resting from the fatigues of its night flight, and it may have slept part of this time. During the course of this twenty minutes it became bright daylight, and I was able to identify the bird as a Nashville warbler. At the end of this twenty minutes, it seemed to revive, began to hop about the tree, and obviously found some insects to eat; then it began to sing, and in a minute or two it proceeded to fly north, presumably at least as far as the woods in the distance. The impression, of course, was that it had had sufficient rest.

The price that these small birds pay for this type of physical activity is that they are very short-lived; they burn themselves out, so to speak, in a comparatively brief span of years. Less active birds, of the less specialized orders, of greater antiquity, with lower body temperatures, live much longer.

In addition to this physical energy, birds obviously have

a very vivid emotional life, but there are many curious contradictions and paradoxes.

The outstanding emotion of birds throughout the greater part of the year is fear. There is no evidence of suspense. It is true, for instance, that our small, migrating land-birds are followed north on their journey by the sharp-shinned hawk, which lives on them, but it would be most incorrect to suppose that the lives of these little creatures are clouded by the constant fear of being caught by the hawk! On the other hand, the stupidity of certain of the older groups of birds is so great as to be positively astonishing.

Returning, however, to the warblers and the sharp-shinned hawk, I remember a day in Central Park, New York City, when I was looking over a flock of warblers in the tree tops, and, to my great delight, I discovered a Cape May warbler, at that time a great rarity in the eastern states. A second later the birds all froze, the singing stopped, and a sharp-shinned hawk dashed into the tree, caught and killed one of them, and flew off with it to a near-by oak. The birds remained immobile and silent for less than a minute, and, in spite of the fact that the hawk was in plain sight and was devouring the warbler which it had just caught, the remaining warblers began to move about in the top of the tree and sing; it would appear that the incident had been completely forgotten.

Excitement and curiosity are outstanding features of the emotional life of birds, and sometimes are carried to a degree which produces fatal results. Normally shy birds can often be potshot when mating. Some years ago, while motoring down a country road in New Jersey, I was diverted by the folly of a chicken that kept running down one gutter of the road ahead of the car, never having sense enough to turn to one side, and always trying to keep well ahead. At a certain stage in these proceedings I suddenly discovered that well ahead of me, sound asleep in an apple tree on a branch overhanging the road, was a red-tailed hawk. So I stopped the car, and looked at the hawk. In the meantime the chicken ambled down the roadside, and when it got directly underneath the hawk, it saw the hawk; it looked up at it, craned its neck a couple of times, and said: "Cluck, cluck, cluck, cluck," in great excitement, whereupon the hawk opened one eye, and without bothering to spread its wings fell down on the chicken, which naturally met a speedy doom! This, I think, is a good illustration of stupidity and curiosity combined.

Excitement in birds can reach the point of extreme anger. Birds can fly into a towering rage with other birds, because of some factor which displeases them, and in addition to these blind rages there is a marked degree of jealousy between the males of any one species in adjacent areas in the breeding season. One of the curious features about birds is their antipathy to certain other species of birds, in a great many cases apparently without any rhyme or reason. Those people who run zoological gardens or who engage in the hobby of aviculture have learned that under no circumstances must certain species ever be put together in the same flight cage, no matter how large.

An outstanding illustration is the antipathy that blue

jays have for all owls. Heaven knows why jays don't like owls. We haven't a single definite or authentic record, so far as I know, that any owl ever did any blue jay the slightest harm; but, it is perfectly obvious that jays detest owls on sight, and that they mob them whenever they discover them.

When it comes to death, extraordinary danger, and what human beings would call tragedy, it is astonishing how it all passes in a few minutes, all recollection seems to fade, and apparently no scar of any kind is left.

In spite of the vivid emotional life of birds, and in spite of their extreme acuity of hearing compared to that of human beings, the degree of their indifference in certain circumstances is positively incredible. In the last world war, there were many observations all going to prove conclusively that the nesting birds on the battle-fronts were much less affected and upset by the shellfire than were the human beings. At one time I was stationed in a small village back of the Second Army Front, and my dugout happened to be facing a little country churchyard with quite a variety of shrubbery. Under the somewhat dreary surroundings I got a certain amount of enjoyment out of a robin redbreast which sang nearly all day long in the shrubbery in this churchyard. On a certain morning the Germans shelled us with 13-inch T.N.T. shells; there was a shell every five minutes for about two and a half hours; the base hospital was struck, various people were killed and wounded, and the survivors cowered in their dugouts, hoping for the best. One of these shells fell right through the roof of the church, blew it apart, and filled the garden with rubbish. Seven minutes after the last shell had fallen the robin redbreast climbed up to the top of one of the remaining bushes and began to sing, recovering from the occasion very much more rapidly than I was able to do myself.

Turning to the sex life of birds, it must be stated in no uncertain terms that the stories current in earlier years of devotion and faithfulness to the mate and young are largely "bunk" in the great majority of birds. The more usual behavior patterns can only be described as exceedingly low, provided we remember that there is no "standard," no code of ethics.

Mr. Baldwin spent ten years in studying the house wrens on his estate near Cleveland, Ohio. He had up to forty-two pairs in various boxes per season, and he banded every single adult and every young bird that was raised on that estate. The marriage relations of the house wren can only be described in human terms as something positively scandalous!

An acquaintance of mine made a very interesting, but somewhat cruel experiment some years ago with the indigo bunting. Finding a nesting pair near his house, he proceeded to shoot the male. The next day the female had secured another male, that sang in the same territory claimed by the first mate. He proceeded to shoot the second male. This kept on until he had shot *nine different* male indigo buntings, and he left the tenth male to help the female raise her family. This experiment suggests two different things. There are a larger number of un-mated birds wandering around the country in the breeding season than ordinary observation would lead one to suspect. But, as far as the sex life of the indigo bunting is concerned, what would we think of a woman who had ten husbands in one summer?

We have here ideal illustrations of the need for caution given at the opening of the chapter. The use of the term "faithfulness" is actually inadmissible. Marital fidelity in human beings implies prior agreement on a code of morality or ethics, and an undertaking to live up to it on the part of the married couple. Who can seriously suppose that any such premises or undertakings exist when two birds pair off in the breeding season? Certain parrots and swans, and perhaps eagles, are supposed to pair for life, but surely not because they subscribe to the principle of monogamy. Nevertheless there are some sentimental lovers of birds who are much irritated when science refuses to endow them with human moral attributes.

Coming, now, to what we might call capacity in birds, I must report that there is remarkably little outside of the standard pattern of behavior for any given species. There would appear to be little free will or choice in conduct. In spite of this extremely limited range of capacity, we have been able in certain cases to determine that there is some individual variation in capacity, as well as considerable specific variation. There are again some strange paradoxes.

The question of sex recognition in birds has received a certain amount of attention in recent years, and many ingenious and interesting experiments have been performed. To sum up the results of these experiments, there is apparently no sex recognition whatever in birds throughout the year, except at the time of the breeding season. In those birds in which the sexes are alike, or nearly alike, from our point of view, it is very clear that the only way the bird recognizes the sex of another individual of its own species is on the basis of a behavior pattern. In tame pigeons, for instance, to use a homely illustration, the male pigeon bows, struts, coos, and spreads his tail before all the pigeons near by, and he recognizes a female pigeon by the way she reacts to his performance. Apparently there is no other means of sex discrimination in these birds.

There are, however, a large variety of our smaller birds where there is marked sexual dimorphism in color. Do the birds themselves distinguish sex by these color differences? A few experiments have been performed which prove that to a certain extent they are able to do so, but at the height of the breeding season only. It is well known that the male flicker has a black facial stripe which is lacking in the female. A mated pair were trapped and banded and a blank paper strip was pasted over the black stripe of the male, whereupon its mate was no longer able to recognize it and forgot about it. The experiment was reversed, with exactly the same result.

In connection with the question of sex recognition, one of the most extraordinary things about birds is their apparent inability to discriminate between a live bird and a dead one. If you present a male of almost any bird in the northern United States with a stuffed female, the stuffed and mounted female is perfectly satisfactory to the male bird. In an experiment which Professor Allen of Cornell performed with grouse, he discovered that if he presented a male ruffed grouse in breeding condition with the skin of a male ruffed grouse which was laid on the ground, this prostrate condition of the dead grouse was "female behavior" to the male grouse, and, consequently, it was perfectly acceptable for mating purposes. On another occasion he presented the male grouse with a stuffed and mounted female grouse, and the male grouse beat this mounted female until the tail broke off, then the head broke off at the neck and hung down by a mere thread, and finally most of the feathers of the back came out; but none of this had any effect in reducing the attractiveness of the dead grouse to the male!

Experiments of the same nature have been tried with red-winged blackbirds, with rather interesting results. On a breeding territory in early spring the males arrive before the females have come. There are two kinds of male blackbirds. There are the younger ones who are about to start their first breeding season, and there are the older males who have bred before. A mounted female proves satisfactory to the birds that are only one year old, but it is not satisfactory to the birds that are two years old, and have had previous experience, so to speak, with a real live female.

The ability of the house wren to discriminate between sexes is zero, when it comes to a dead mounted bird. A row of mounted wrens has been put in front of a male house wren, one of them a female house wren, the second a winter wren, which is closely like a house wren, and the third a marsh wren, which is very different from a house wren. The male house wren was not able to distinguish between the dead house wren and the winter wren, but it paid no attention to the marsh wren.

These experiments show the strange paradoxes in avian capacity and perception.

Experiments have been tried on birds as regards their ability to count. With ducks and grouse, which have very large broods of young, it is quite clear that the female is entirely unable to keep track of the total number of her original brood. It is the business of the young to keep track of the mother, and it is just too bad for one of them if it does not do so. The following experiment has been tried with small songbirds. If one egg has been laid in the nest and it is removed, all are able to perceive the loss of the egg. If, however, two eggs have been laid and one of them is taken away, the majority of birds are apparently unable to perceive that anything is missing. Those birds that are able to count up to three are exceedingly few and far between.

Birds seem to have surprisingly little power of choice in conduct and behavior in the great majority of directions. They seldom try to flirt with a type of food which is not the natural and normal one for their species. A few years ago ninety per cent of all the individuals of the brant goose in existence on the Atlantic side of the New World perished because of the strange eel-grass blight, which was so widely discussed and talked about. The brant had exceedingly specialized food habits, subsisted primarily on eel-grass, and when the eel-grass died off most of the brant perished of starvation. The survivors, however, learned to find other things to eat, and they found those other things by imitating ducks and other geese, and the species was possibly saved from extinction, in part, by that means.

There is a primitive sense of language in birds. It is clear that various notes of birds express a few of the more primary emotions. Alarm and distress notes are generally understood by a great variety of species. Noisy and alert birds like the yellow-legs and kingfisher act as a warning of the approach of danger, not only to other birds, but even to mammals and crocodiles.

The distinction between dangerous and harmless hawks is another outstanding capacity of birds, undoubtedly due to their great acuity of vision. The birds usually signal the presence of these hawks to the bird student before he has gotten around to seeing them for himself. Here is another paradox in avian powers of perception. They can discover the dangerous hawk at an extraordinary distance, but they do not seem to care or notice whether the bird is alive or a stuffed one mounted on a perch. Jays will mob a stuffed owl indefinitely.

We now come to the much-mooted subject of intelligence, and here two common terms, as the naturalist uses them, must be carefully defined. There is a great deal of talk about the instincts of birds, and the question arises: What is an instinct? The current definition is that it is the inherited capacity or propensity to perform seemingly rational acts without conscious design or instruction. A typical example is the ability of a bird only one year old to build a most elaborate, complex, and beautiful nest, without, of course, having received any instruction. It is obviously able to do it perfectly the very first time. The proper care and feeding of the young also seems to be purely instinctive in birds, as is their knowledge of a long migration route over which they travel for the first time.

Intelligence, on the other hand, is quickness of understanding as distinct from perception, the power of reasoning, drawing an inference, or working out advantageous conduct under difficult or novel conditions.

Again, a great deal of nonsense has been written and spoken about birds in this connection. Bird lovers and popular writers have endowed birds with human-like intelligence, and they have even invented a sixth sense to account for some of the things that they do. On the other hand, a particularly cold-blooded and hard-boiled group of physiologists and animal behaviorists have denied anything to birds whatsoever, except instinct. According to this school, all their activities are purely instinctive, and birds are, consequently, to be thought of as feathered automatons. The real truth would appear to be very much nearer No. 2 than No. 1 of these two propositions. It must be admitted that some primitive birds come exceedingly close to being feathered automatons, and there is no experimental evidence whatsoever of anything remotely resembling reasoning power in birds.

Memory is remarkably good in certain very limited directions, for instance, in direction-finding. An interesting case is afforded by various small birds which are victimized by the cowbird. The cowbird egg is differently colored from most of them. It is also very much larger, but the alien egg is not recognized as such by the great majority of birds. There are a few exceptions. It is recognized by the house wren or by most house wrens, who get rid of it by stabbing it with their bills. The yellow warbler is one of the few out of seventy-five victims of the cowbird in the eastern United States that also can recognize the strange egg, and it disposes of it by building a second nest on top of the nest that contains the cowbird egg. The red-eyed vireo provides an interesting example of individual variation. Some red-eyed vireos are unable to recognize the alien egg; other red-eyed vireos are able to do so, and take one means or another of getting rid of it. We have here a question to solve, if only the necessary coöperation could be secured. It would be interesting to find out if those red-eyed vireos that can distinguish the alien cowbird egg are individuals which had been victimized by the cowbird in some preceding year! 1102586

Birds learn by experience, but very slowly indeed, and by an obvious method of trial and error, rather than by reasoning out the solution of a problem. In the great majority of difficulties, dangers, and novel situations which the white man and his civilization have brought upon birds, it has taken at least twenty-five generations for the birds to adapt themselves to any one of them. The semi-domestication of the robin is an interesting illustration in point. It has proceeded only part way. There are still a few robins which are as wild as their ancestors ever were, nesting in the deep forest in a shy and retiring manner in the north woods. Some city and town robins which have become semi-domesticated have, obviously, degenerated in many ways as the result of this domestication, and they exhibit stupidity, carelessness, and lack of competence in various directions.

A familiar illustration is the chicken and the arrival of the automobile. When I was a boy and the motoring age first began forty years ago in this country, it was a routine thing to kill, run over or "flatten out" chickens, as it was called, in the course of every afternoon drive. It took just about twenty-five generations of chickens for this severe and constant mortality to disappear to a comparatively small and negligible percentage.

In a great many birds, however, the capacity to learn something new by experience is almost zero. Boobies, for instance, are tropical sea-birds which nest on remote and lonely islets; sailors used to land from a boat and club the boobies to death for fresh meat while the remaining boobies stared solemnly at the proceedings, and waited for their turn to die. It rarely occurred to them to move or to fly away!

My wife and I visited a big colony of boobies some years ago on Galera Island, one of the Pearl Islands off Panama. As the boat approached the island, boobies became common, and their tameness and curiosity were immediately obvious. One of them lit in the shrouds to look us over, with every sign of goggling curiosity and amazement. A

Allan D. Cruickshank

WOOD IBIS ROOST

On mangrove key, south Florida

John H. Gerard

BANDING A FAMILY OF BARN OWLS

Who made their home in a grain elevator at Godfrey, Illinois

few seconds later it flew even nearer, and one of the crew was able to jump into the air and catch it alive on the wing. I cannot honestly say that this booby showed any real sign of fear or perturbation when it was actually caught and held in the hand. As we landed on the island and went to the breeding colony, the birds were entirely indifferent to our approach. My wife was able to secure a portrait at less than five feet.

The plume-bearing egret was brought to the verge of extinction thirty years ago; it became so exceedingly shy that the discharge of a rifle a mile from a breeding rookery would cause all the egrets to dash wildly into the air. In the meantime, the fish crows, which always hang about egret rookeries to get a meal off the eggs or the young, were perfectly able to discriminate the fact that the rifle was in fact a mile away and, consequently, involved no danger at all, so they would remain in the rookery and would get a fine meal while the egrets wasted their time flying violently about.

The brown pelicans on the east coast of Florida had a famous breeding island called Pelican Island. It was raided by angry fishermen several seasons in succession. The pelicans were about to be exterminated; whereupon the Audubon Society and the federal government combined; Pelican Island was made a sanctuary; and a big sign was put up saying: "This is Pelican Island. The Pelicans are protected, and no one can land on this island without a permit." When the pelicans returned the following year to their island and saw the sign, they said: "This is terrible, we are not used to this sign at all." And they deserted the reservation in a body!

Ducks also show curious anomalies in their capacity to learn by experience. It is obvious that in the course of time they can learn the range of a shotgun, and they are able to adapt their behavior to the hunting season and change back rapidly when it closes. On Cayuga Lake, many years ago, canvasback were common, arriving on the lake in early November; but, as the banks of the lake were rocky and steep, canvasback shooting was very poor and disappointing. In those days the season ended on the 10th of January. Either on the 13th or sometimes the 12th of January, the canvasback were way up the canal in the heart of the city of Ithaca, diving for the bread crusts which the passers-by tossed from a bridge.

Professor Allen captured native wild ducks, pinioned them, and kept them in a pen. He alone came to the pen to feed them, and it happened that he always wore rubber boots. Most of the ducks gradually learned to recognize the feeder, *provided he wore his boots*. They learned they could not fly, ceased to dash wildly about the pen, and finally did not object to being caught and examined, as they learned that no harm resulted. The wood duck was, however, apparently hopelessly stupid and never learned anything.

Interesting evidence has been derived from certain experiments where birds are submitted to a conflict of primary emotions or instincts. Professor Allen's well-known experiment with a pair of redstarts and their young is a good illustration. At a time when the feeding instinct of the parent birds was at its height, and the young required the maximum amount of care and attention, a confederate took the young out of the nest and held them in his hand on the lawn. The question arises: "What did the parent birds do?" In this particular case the male came and fed the young, but the female would not do so. If we stop there for a moment, what interpretation do we put on these events? Was there any intelligence, and on the part of which sex? I do not see that there is any definite answer to this question. You could argue it both ways. Some people would say the "brave and noble" little male redstart conquered his fear of the dreadful human being, and stuck to his young, and that the female was cowardly and would not. On the other hand, you could argue that the female was the more intelligent of the two sexes; with her instinctive and well-earned fear of man, she played safe and did not take any chances. This experiment has been repeated with various birds many times with varying results. In one case, it is the male that feeds the young, and the female will not; again, the female feeds the young and the male will not. Sometimes both parents feed the young, and on occasion the young are at once entirely abandoned.

There is a sequel to this experiment which is by no means rare. In the case of the redstarts, for instance, the female of which would not feed the young, she discovered a near-by nest of another species, where the young were at about the same stage of development as her own, and she worked off her feeding instinct by feeding the young of the strange species. There was, consequently, no question of intelligence whatever, so far as I can see. The more powerful emotion, fear, completely erased from the mind of this female redstart all memory of her own young, and she never paid any further attention to them, even after they were put back in the nest and her own mate continued to look after them.

Observations leading to similar conclusions have been made over and over again. There is the so-called "suicide" of wounded ducks. The use of the word is, of course, most improper, because there is no departure from a normal ethical standard on the part of the duck. What actually happens is that the wounded duck has such a mortal fear of being captured by the hunter, or his retriever dog, that this is the dominant emotion of the moment, and, consequently, to escape capture it seizes hold of some vegetation or roots underneath the water and stays there until drowned. Just as the term "suicide" is entirely improper when applied to birds, so, if I may revert to the redstart for a moment, is the term "desertion" of the young. Desertion implies a moral obliquity. It is an unfavorable and a critical term which cannot fairly be applied to birds at all.

Years ago I used to visit Gardiner's Island at the eastern end of Long Island, and one fall there was a plague of mice on this island. As a result, hawks of a great variety of species had gathered on the island, and were in astonishing abundance for birds of that group. An ignorant and stupid man was the superintendent of the estate and he was much exercised over these hawks, fearing for his chickens and pheasants. He was well aware that there was a plague of mice, but he never thought that the hawks and mice had any connection. So he had erected a series of pole-traps all over the hills on the island, and when my friend and I arrived, there was an unfortunate hawk with a crushed foot hanging from each of a considerable number of these pole-traps. After persuading the superintendent that the hawks would be the only means of reducing his plague of mice, we proceeded to make a tour of the pole-traps to release the hawks. In one place, close together, were five traps, with five hawks dangling from them, all within plain sight of each other. Every hawk fought like mad while being rescued, used its wings to beat my face, endeavored to bite me with its bill, and made it as difficult as possible for me to release it from the trap. After four hawks had been released, tossed in the air, and had flown away, the fifth hawk had perceived nothing, learned nothing, and fought just as bitterly to prevent its rescue as the others preceding it. The emotion, fear, was dominant over the perceptive powers of the hawk.

Robins and other small birds sometimes have tragic accidents, due to various unexpected causes. One day, in my garden, a great outcry arose among the robins. Various other birds clucked and called in excitement, and I stepped out of the house to see what was up. I discovered a robin hanging by one foot, which had been caught in a mass of string in a lilac bush. Taking hold of the robin and doing my best to unsnarl its foot and release it was the last straw, and it died of fright in my hand, a post mortem dissection showing that the physiological cause had been a cerebral hemorrhage.

Another experiment yielding astonishing results was performed by Professor Allen of Cornell. In this particular case there were two male song sparrows nesting in adjacent territories. A very common thing in birds of the same species is that there is a hierarchy of dominant and weaker individuals. One male sparrow was dominant and the other was weak. The weak male would, under no circumstances, trespass on the territory of the dominant male. So he was trapped and put in a cage and the cage was deposited in the territory of the dominant male. Ludicrous and extraordinary results took place. In the first place, the dominant male fell into a rage, attacked the cage, and made every effort to get at the captive song sparrow, apparently unable to reach the conclusion that on account of the bars of the cage it could not do so, and that the situation was hopeless. All that the weak male had to do was to stay quietly in the middle of its cage, and let the other sparrow rage outside. But it was wild with fear, and dashed madly around the inside of the cage, while the other song sparrow dashed madly about on the outside. By a combination of circumstances, the wing-tip feathers of the weak male inside the cage happened to project for an instant through the bars, and the feathers were grabbed in the bill of the male outside. Whereupon the weaker male immediately died of fright and expired on the floor of the cage. Its death made no difference whatsoever to the song sparrow outside, who kept on just as madly trying to get at it, and beating against the bars of the cage as before. This absurd and unintelligent behavior merely proves that these two birds were motivated entirely by one or the other of two powerful emotions.

The late Professor Ritter made a careful study of the California woodpecker. It is noted for its habit of storing acorns for winter food, and its method is to cut holes of just the right size and jam the acorns in. While most industrious and active in its storing, much of this activity is a purely instinctive reaction, as is proved by the fact that the whereabouts of many of the acorns is forgotten, the place never revisited. One "foolish" bird found a knothole of just the right size in the side wall of a locked cabin. It spent all fall creating a huge pile of acorns on the floor inside, and was never able to perceive that it could not possibly get at any of them again, that the effort was entirely wasted.

Parrots and members of the crow family are easily the most intelligent of birds. In spite of the wealth of amusing stories, however, I have yet to hear of a "talking" parrot where it was *absolutely certain* that it knew what it was saying, except in a few most elementary directions. Most of this "talking" is clever mimicry, aided by indispensable equipment, a fleshy and flexible tongue, for enunciation. Jays and magpies are capable of clever thieving. Ravens have been known to combine forces to capture prey too big or too fast for one bird. A pair of ravens have "ganged up" on a weasel and killed it; they have also taken turns chasing a thrush until it was exhausted and killed it. I know of no authenticated cases suggesting a higher intellectual capacity than this in birds.

REFERENCES

1. BALDWIN, S. PRENTISS. Marriage Relations of the House Wren. *Auk*, 1921, pp. 228–237.
2. NOBLE, G. KINGSLEY. Courtship and Sexual Selection of the Flicker. *Auk*, 1936, pp. 269–282.
3. NOBLE, G. K., and VOGT, W. An Experimental Study of Sex Recognition in Birds. *Auk*, 1935, pp. 278–286.
4. ALLEN, A. A. Sex Rhythm in the Ruffed Grouse, and Other Birds. *Auk*, 1934, pp. 180–199.
5. RITTER, WILLIAM. *The California Woodpecker and I.* Berkeley: University of California Press, 1938.

CHAPTER III

ADAPTABILITY OF BIRDS

BIRDS resemble mammals, and many other animals for that matter, in the great range of variation displayed in their powers of adaptation to new and strange conditions or a suddenly changed environment. Such changes have been taking place throughout geological time, and they have always proved fatal to the majority. We must remember that far more species of mammals and birds have become extinct in the past than the total now living on earth. Today the upsets and dangers brought about by mankind are merely an added difficulty in surviving. The Age of Mammals has already passed into history; certain of our larger and more conspicuous birds are doomed unless special protection serves to preserve a remnant.

One reason for extinction has always been the fact that most animals are *specialized*, either in structure or habits, often in both. It is the irony of evolution that the successful adaptations of today, which enable an animal to fit into and flourish in a certain environment, are fatal handicaps when the environment changes. Philosophically, there is often only a hairline between adaptation and specialization; it is really a point of view rather than a fact, and the criterion is the relative success or failure of the moment.

Flightless birds are specialized to the point of invariable disaster with the arrival of man. Birds that eat only mistletoe berries are specialized as compared to those which are omnivorous. Many birds have remarkably shaped bills, and can consequently only obtain a certain food in a certain way. Is this structure an advantageous adaptation or is it a case of extreme specialization? Who can tell, until it is finally settled in the remote future by the ultimate test of survival or extinction?

So far as can be inferred from observation, birds, as a class of vertebrates, run the entire gamut between extreme specialization and great adaptability. Many birds are extremely specialized and have no powers of adaptation whatever; moreover it is often a matter of temperament, a total lack of initiative or the capacity to make an effort to survive. This is a very different thing from special anatomical structures which automatically restrict behavior and activity to certain narrow and rigid patterns. Here the die was cast, so to speak, in a past geological age; it is all or nothing now, the special structures work well or they do not.

In certain ways the most interesting cases of all are those where interference by man has not been a primary factor. They are, naturally enough, very rare and difficult to authenticate.

Possibly the world's record for no adaptability is furnished by a flightless rail which formerly lived on Wake Island in the central Pacific. Fortunately Dr. Wetmore has given us a graphic picture of it before its final extinction.

A distinct species, it must have been on this tiny island a very long time. Wake Island is a typical coral reef. There is an outside barrier reef, an inner lagoon, in the center of which are three small, low sandy islands, with uniform vegetation, which are connected by flats at low tide. The remarkable discovery about this flightless rail made by the naturalists who visited Wake Island was that it was confined to two of these islands only. Twice every day, for countless millenniums, it might just as well have walked across the flats to the third island, but it was never known to have done so.

An example of the opposite extreme in adaptability carried to an almost miraculous extent is the case of the black-browed albatross, or molly-mawk of the cold southern temperate oceans, one of the great travelers and wanderers of the world. One specimen of this albatross has been shot northwest of the island of Spitzbergen only four degress from the North Pole, and it was consequently 7,000 miles or so out of its range. Another individual turned up on the Faroe Islands, north of Great Britain and halfway to Iceland, where, entirely alone, it consorted with the colony of nesting gannets on the island. The bird became well known to the natives, was seen by various visiting naturalists, and spent the summer on the cliffs among the gannets. It must have spent the winter at sea with them, rather than have gone to the southern hemisphere and back again. For *thirty-four consecutive years* this albatross spent each summer with the gannets on the same cliff, until it was finally shot; and it is now preserved in one of the museums in Denmark. This is a truly remarkable and marvelous case of adaptability. The bird was 7,000 miles away from home; it was at the opposite end of the earth; its food must have been substantially different; the climate was most assuredly different; and the seasons, of course, were completely reversed. To have lived so long it must have been healthy, and one can only speculate about what happened to the annual reproductive cycle.

In the historical period birds have suffered chiefly because their environment or living conditions have been radically or abruptly changed by man. The flightless rail is an example of the extreme specialization characteristic of island birds, especially the birds of small oceanic islands, as compared with those of larger land masses. The conditions are uniform, and very limited, of necessity. In a regrettable number of cases the slightest alteration of the original primeval conditions on these small islands has been disastrous to the specialized land-birds that inhabit them. They have been used to one set of living conditions for so long that they cannot tolerate any other. My remarks apply with equal force to other groups of animals and even to some plants. Most of the species of birds which have become extinct in the historic periods are birds of smaller islands, and it would be no exaggeration to say that all island faunas are in constant danger from the white man's civilization.

There is a peculiar subfamily of little songbirds, known as the Hawaiian honey-eaters or the Drepanids, chiefly confined to the mountain rain forests of the Hawaiian

Islands. Their scarlet and yellow feathers were used to make the famous cloaks of the Hawaiian kings. In recent years many of these mountain forests have been turned into state parks, with the idea that they would be preserved from destruction, fire, and lumbering, and that the fascinating flora, the remarkable land snails, and the peculiar birds would survive. According to the usual policy of the United States government, roads and trails were built, so that the public could have access to these spots of scenic beauty and interest. It is reliably reported that these Hawaiian honey-eaters, or at least some of them, accustomed for thousands of years to a practically sunless and dripping forest, would under no circumstances cross the open space that had come into existence by building a road. The range of each individual was cut in half, and perhaps too many males were left on one side of the road, and too many females on the other.

Another thing that has worked havoc with a great many island species is the introduction of other birds of a more vigorous stock. These birds, or animals, sometimes cause untold ruin to the original native fauna, which cannot successfully compete with them.

On Chatham Island, a treeless island south of New Zealand in the Antipodes, there were a few peculiar and highly modified land-birds living under very bleak conditions. When white men arrived and looked Chatham Island over, and tried to figure out to what possible use it could be put, they decided that the only thing that could be done was to try to raise sheep. So they introduced sheep, and the sheep resulted in the rapid extermination of the majority of the land-birds, by destroying the cover of tall grass in which they lived and by trampling on the nests and young.

An even more remarkable case is the desert and mountainous island of Guadeloupe, off the coast of Lower California, Mexico. The lowlands are desert, but the mountain peaks are high enough to get some moisture, and there is, consequently, a varied flora and a cedar forest at higher altitudes. Most unfortunately, one of the earliest ships to visit Guadeloupe Island had goats on board, and some of these goats were released and ran wild. They multiplied and throve, and gradually ate up every single living thing on the island, always moving higher and higher up the mountain as the desert vegetation got used up at lower altitudes. Finally, there was practically nothing left but the cedar forest, and in some incredible manner the goats learned to climb the trees, and photographs are in existence of a flock of goats wandering out over the terminal branches of these gigantic old cedars, browsing on the needles. The result was that a substantial percentage of the native birds on Guadeloupe Island have become extinct.

In New Zealand the original colonists found the local birds scarce, shy, and uninteresting, and, as a matter of sentiment, they introduced from England some of the commonest and best beloved of British birds, like the song thrush, the blackbird, the sky-lark, the robin redbreast, and the linnet. These birds, transplanted to New Zealand, throve amazingly, and some of them developed brand new and utterly unexpected habits. The song thrush became carnivorous, and began to eat the eggs and young of the native birds. The introduction of these foreign birds spelled disaster to many of the natives, which have completely disappeared, or now survive only in remote mountain forests or on special island reservations where the introduced British birds have not penetrated.

It might prove of interest to analyze the causes back of the extinction or great decrease in numbers of certain North American birds which have attracted popular attention. While persecution by man has always been the main cause, I can show that in most cases one kind of specialization or another has been a strong contributing factor. The Labrador duck is the only bird so little known at the time of its final disappearance (1865–1875) that we have no idea as to the cause. We do not even know that the report of its nesting in Labrador was correct. There is no evidence that it was a popular game bird, or that it was extensively shot, and it was definitely poor eating.

The great auk had the hopeless handicap of being flightless. It was consequently an ideal source of supply for fresh meat for whaling and fishing vessels, and the breeding colonies were constantly raided.

The Eskimo curlew was tame and unsuspicious, was easy to shoot, and was delicious eating. It had a tremendous migration route with long nonstop ocean flights, like those of the golden plover and Hudsonian godwit, described later. A relatively small population could not stand the toll of this migration route and hunting combined. The other two shore-birds were reduced to the verge of extinction at the same time for the same reasons.

The final extinction of the heath hen was due to a combination of factors. It was formerly found in the sandy plains and pine barrens of the eastern states from southern Maine to New Jersey and western Pennsylvania. It was shot and hunted for food throughout the year for a couple of centuries, but, in addition to the hunting, its numbers were reduced by the frequent forest fires which resulted from the white man's occupation of the country. For many years it survived only on the island of Martha's Vineyard, where a reservation was established for it, and there was a gratifying and satisfactory increase until a particularly disastrous forest fire decimated it. The final cause of its extinction was apparently an unbalanced ratio of females among the survivors. This is fatal to many game birds, because the unmated individuals become rogues and pester the successful females unmercifully, kill the young, and smash the eggs.

The passenger pigeon is an excellent illustration of a dangerously specialized bird, suddenly coming into contact with disaster in the form of the white man's civilization. Not only did it migrate in incredible multitudes, but unfortunately it nested in gigantic colonies, also. The late Dr. Jonathan Dwight of New York, an ornithologist of the older generation, often told me of his visit to the last great nesting in southern Michigan. In a certain beech and oak forest there were about two and a half million pairs of passenger pigeons, nesting in an area of several square

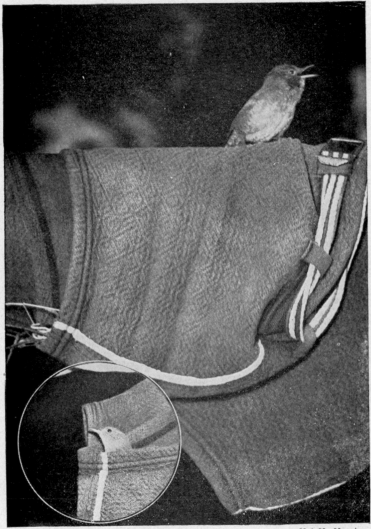

Hal H. Harrison

HOUSE WREN HOME IN SWIMMING TRUNKS
The birds took immediate possession and proceeded to raise their brood.

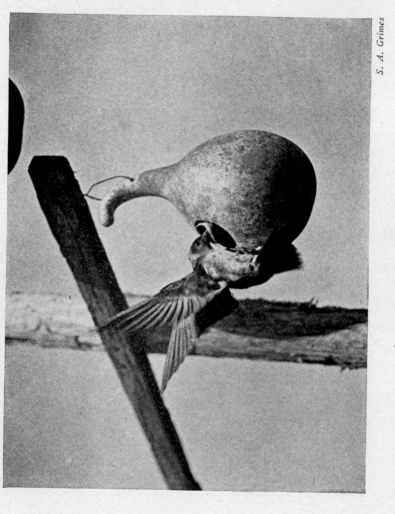

S. A. Grimes

PURPLE MARTIN'S GOURD NEST

miles. They built the flimsiest nests of twigs, so thin that one could see often the eggs from the ground through the interstices. There was a constant roar of arriving and departing birds. Every time a gun was fired or there was any kind of a disturbance, several hundred thousand pigeons dashed wildly into the air, the nests were broken, and one could hear the splashing and the popping of the eggs in every direction. If any accident occurred to the one egg that a pair of passenger pigeons laid, there was apparently no second try that season. Men hunted and pursued these pigeons day and night, throughout the breeding season, and it is believed that over one million birds were shipped in barrels to the New York market. This very naturally sounded the death knell of the passenger pigeon. However, one of the important contributing factors was its highly specialized and dangerous breeding habits and poor egg-laying capacity.

The Carolina parakeet became extinct because of persecution by man. It was sought for as a cage bird, but, like most parrots, it was exceedingly destructive to agricultural crops. It has been related, and is undoubtedly correct, that as a corn field was ripening and the corn was coming into the milk, these parakeets would descend upon the field and in no time at all every ear would be stripped or damaged. One can hardly blame our colonial ancestors for having the very strongest objections to them. So the Carolina parakeet was mercilessly shot and hunted. Most unfortunately, it was tame and confiding in its disposition, and if one fired into a flock of these parakeets, and two or three birds fell, wounded, to the ground and flopped, the rest of the flock would turn and come flying back over their wounded companions, so that sometimes it was possible to get the entire flock.

The ivory-billed woodpecker illustrates a bird which simply could not adapt itself to the slightest change in its conditions. It requires a wilderness. It requires a great many trees of just the right age and an extensive feeding territory, because it feeds on a very limited variety of insects and boring beetles. In addition it appears to have a very poor sex rhythm; a high percentage of the eggs are infertile, and Dr. Tanner found that breeding pair after breeding pair would fail to raise a single young bird.

The red-head duck is one of the North American ducks which have decreased in the last half century, but the red-head has decreased in proportion very much more seriously than the majority, for two reasons. In the first place, a higher percentage of its original breeding territory was far south and was, consequently, destroyed by agriculture in the central and northwestern states. Moreover it is particularly tame. Over and over again I have had red-heads come in from salt to fresh water to drink, and they would give me the impression of rushing to the blind and the decoys as fast as they possibly could, to get shot. They never learned to reconnoiter, to fly high over the decoys, to make up their minds if all were well; the hunting season, therefore, has been more disastrous for the red-head than it was for most other ducks.

The magnificent whooping crane is another bird which

will probably become extinct in a comparatively few years, and here we lack an adequate life-history study to find out exactly what all the causes may be. The first thing that caused a great decrease in this bird was the drainage of two-thirds of its original breeding range in the central states, which are now part of what is known as the corn belt. But the survivors have apparently found a new breeding area, much farther to the north, and this remnant disappears into the Arctic to nest, we do not know exactly where. Just why the survivors have not succeeded in maintaining their numbers is something I cannot explain, but there is no evidence whatsoever in the last quarter of a century that hunting or destruction by man has been a material factor.

Four relatively little-known North American hawks, called kites because they have a notched or forked tail, have sadly and rapidly decreased in the historical period, chiefly because of their extreme tameness and lack of suspicion. Most unfortunately any evilly disposed person can walk up to any kite and potshot it off its perch, in spite of one hundred years of this type of experience. While the white man and his civilization are primarily responsible for the decrease of the kites, part of the reason is their absolute inability to learn anything new and to gain the wariness and suspicion of which they are so desperately in need.

To turn to a more cheerful theme, there are far more cases of adaptability and success than failure. In this country, bird lovers have no use for the introduced starling (1890) and the house sparrow (1850–1875), but the latter is, perhaps, the outstanding and most successful songbird in the world. It is now successfully naturalized from New-foundland to Havana, Cuba; it thrives in every section of the United States, including the California deserts below sea level. It is at home in Mexico, in the tropical Hawaiian Islands, Chile, and New Zealand. It has conquered almost every climate on earth except the Arctic. We admire the Pilgrim fathers who first landed in Massachusetts, and we know what a terrible time they had surviving, in particular, their first winter—a bitter cold of which they never dreamed, and which they had never experienced in their native land. The house sparrows and the starlings, however, had exactly the same difficulties to face in their turn, when they were introduced, and they survived even colder win-ters. As starlings are highly migratory birds, they had to learn a brand new migration route in a strange continent. The first record for Mexico of the starling has recently been published. Moreover, the starling competes success-fully with all native species that use the same nesting site as it does.

Consider the competition between the house sparrow and the bluebird, and the amazing adaptability of the house sparrow which, in default of a natural nesting site, will use branches, vines, electric light hoods, a cranny in a city building, or a shutter fastened against the side wall of the house. But, if the bluebird is driven from its nesting holes by the house sparrow, we cannot conceive of its adopting some other nesting site. It merely fades from that section of territory.

Another way in which birds show adaptive powers is their ability to learn that a great many of the remarkable features of the white man's civilization do them no manner of harm, or can even be used to advantage. Wild ducks at the height of the hunting season, when they are at their wariest and shyest, will pay no attention whatever to the express train, roaring by on the bank of the marsh or the lake. In Texas, wild turkeys can always be seen from the express trains going from Houston to Brownsville. They have learned that the train and its noise does them no harm whatsoever, and they do not even bother to run into the bushes to hide. The rough-winged swallow in the Hudson River Valley has found that the culverts built by the New York Central are abounding in holes and crevices and that they furnish very satisfactory nesting sites. There is a long series of culverts north of Poughkeepsie where the walls are fifteen and twenty feet high. Numerous pairs breed in the holes in these culverts every summer, with express and freight trains roaring by every two minutes of the day and night, shaking the entire ground. These would appear to be practically intolerable conditions, but it is obvious that the swallows do not mind them in the least.

In connection with my uncomplimentary remarks on avian intelligence in Chapter II, it should be noted that these adaptations, and others to be mentioned later, have all taken twenty-five to one hundred or more generations to acquire.

Similarly, the killdeer has discovered that freight yards provide excellent nesting sites, where its eggs can be camouflaged. Pairs have been known to return several years in succession and nest in the gravel between two express tracks, utterly indifferent to the trains roaring by, only three feet away.

The barn swallow, the robin, and the phoebe have been known to nest and raise successful broods on moving ferries. In recent decades, sparrow hawks and duck hawks have discovered that our largest cities are excellent places in which to spend the winter, with an adequate food supply of sparrows, starlings, and pigeons. Canada has provided the first record of a pair of duck hawks that remained to nest on the window ledge of an office skyscraper, but the sparrow hawk has been nesting in some of our cities for years.

Many of our commonest birds now live in a state of semi-domestication. Robins prefer the vicinity of man, city parks and suburban gardens. Even in arctic Newfoundland, on the Straits of Belle Isle, the robins have abandoned the clumps of dwarf spruce, and nest on the racks for drying fish near the fishermen's huts, just out of reach of the fierce and ever hungry "huskies." It is difficult to find any, still shy and retiring, living in the deep woods, their ancestral home. "Chimney" swifts now use chimneys; only once have I found them nesting in hollow trees in the forest, and that was on the edge of Lake Drummond in the Great Dismal Swamp of southeastern Virginia. At least twenty-five species of birds still nest in the city of Cambridge, where the bold and fearless crows take a ride up Massachusetts Avenue on the top of the trolley car.

In the crow habits of domestication are in the process

Rodger Harrison

DUCK HAWK'S SKYSCRAPER HOME

Nest box on seventeenth floor of Sun Life Building, Montreal. The duck hawk, once one of our wildest and scarcest hawks, has taken to life in the city where it preys on the pigeons.

Joseph McAree, Courtesy of New York State Nature Association

FISH HAWK'S NESTING POLE

Supplied by the Atlantic City Electric Co., with double arms placed to make building easier. Previously the fish hawks, nesting on poles carrying wires, had caused short circuits by dragging twigs across the wires.

of being acquired. Around Boston the crow is a city and suburban dweller; it is virtually absent from New York City. Geographically the situation is reversed in the wood thrush. Around Philadelphia every suburban garden plot has had a pair for decades; this habit did not become general around New York until 1920; near Boston only a small percentage of wood thrushes have become suburbanites, but the proportion is increasing annually.

So far as I know the barn swallow is one hundred per cent domesticated; I cannot recall ever having heard of a pair in the northeast using any nesting site but a building in many decades. The cliff swallow has really become the eave swallow, the best way to describe its complete change of nesting site.

The barn owl deserves special comment. It is one of the few land-birds on earth which is nearly cosmopolitan in distribution, and which has become semi-domesticated in most of the continents. Every year in the United States more and more barn owls abandon hollow trees in woods, and use outhouses, sheds, barn lofts, church steeples, and towers of public buildings in our larger cities. The acquisition of this habit in colonial times is particularly remarkable when we consider that the owl was regarded as a bird of ill omen and shot on sight as a matter of principle.

Many birds have learned to make use of materials supplied by man. Cotton, wool, string, twine, horsehair, and paper are all regularly used in nest construction. When yarn of assorted colors has been offered an oriole, it has become choosy and selected a "favorite" shade. There is even a record of a Carolina wren's nest made principally out of hairpins!

The impact of modern civilization on birds can be reduced to general terms. To go back to the past, the civilization of ancient Egypt had no deleterious effect on the abundant bird life of the Nile Valley, but in China there have been substantial readjustments on account of the steady deforestation of a vast area of country over a period of at least two thousand years. Many of the forest-inhabiting birds of China are now, perforce, rare and local, and they are confined to the upper levels of the higher mountains in the remote and less thickly populated sections.

In Europe we know that the white man's civilization developed *very slowly* and *very gradually* over a period of two thousand years or more. Not one single bird of Europe has become extinct in the whole historic period. A small number only have been unable to make any satisfactory adjustment and are, consequently, rare and local, but it is reasonably certain that the white man's civilization appears to make no substantial difference to the great majority of European birds. North America and Australia, however, provide the outstanding cases where civilization arrived very suddenly or relatively very suddenly, compared to Europe, and where, consequently, the original fauna was put to the maximum degree of strain and difficulty. It is, consequently, only in these two continents that any birds have become extinct in the historical period.

It is a common but great mistake to exaggerate the results in North America. The great majority of our birds are more or less adapted to conditions as they are at the moment. A mere handful of birds have become extinct or are vanishing. There is a relatively small group of large and conspicuous species, and of course the game birds, that are in constant need of protection. It is almost always forgotten that every change in habitat which greatly reduces the numbers of some birds in which we are interested has also automatically benefited several birds in which we happen not to be interested. This is the normal psychology of human interest, but it is very poor biology, and it is unsound natural history. When New England was covered with a primeval forest, where do you suppose the hundred common species of birds of our orchards, fields, thickets, and woodland were? When Cape Cod was originally a primeval beech and red oak forest, where were the fifty species of summer residents which are now found in the pitch pine and the scrub oak barrens and in the shade trees and orchards in the vicinity of the various villages? The point is that the number of species which have become adapted to civilization and which may be presumed to have increased their former numbers under primeval conditions is greatly in excess of those which have become extinct, which are vanishing, or which are in need of protection.

One corollary of these remarks is that when this protection is granted them, when half-way intelligent measures of conservation are adopted and are reasonably enforced, the remarkable results which are attained could not possibly have been predicted in advance by the most optimistic promoters of these measures. In the last twenty-five years, the rapid increase of many formerly persecuted species has more than balanced the decreases of the preceding two and a half centuries, and this, in itself, is a tribute to the ability of birds to adapt themselves to improved conditions.

The black-backed and herring gulls are ideal illustrations. When I was a boy, the National Audubon Society was worried for fear that the herring gull would become extinct as a breeding bird in the United States, and the few remaining colonies on the coast of Maine were guarded by a warden, thanks to a special fund. Who worries about these gulls today? As they have multiplied and adapted themselves to civilization, other species of gulls are beginning to learn the same tricks, and now the black-backed gull is on the move. In recent years, not only does it throng our harbors, but it comes to ponds and garbage dumps well inland. It is now nesting in the States, regularly south to Massachusetts, and has already raised young successfully on Long Island. Who knows what this gull is going to do next? It now goes as far south as South Carolina in winter, and occurs regularly on the Great Lakes.

The removal of the shore-birds from the game-bird class has produced astounding results in a group of birds that were so pitifully reduced in my boyhood. A friend of mine, Mr. R. J. Eaton, tells me that on or about the year 1912 he went down to Cape Cod with a friend to have some shore-bird shooting. They got out before daylight, went down to Nauset Point, set out their decoys, and were all ready for the hoped-for flight at dawn. They remained the entire morning. They saw several flocks of small sand-

pipers, three or four ring-necked plovers, and several yel-
lowlegs; to their great joy, a flock of black-bellied plover
went by, and they got three out of five. They had a very
pleasant morning, and they went back to lunch, satisfied at
a most successful trip. Imagine anybody today going off on
a trip for shore-birds if that was all they were going to get
in the way of results! To make a long story short, twenty-
five years of protection has now brought about a condition
whereby one can see more species and more individuals of
shore-birds in one day on the coast of Massachusetts than
could be seen in a solid decade of constant field experience
in my youth!

The National Audubon Society deserves the chief credit
for saving the egrets from extinction, a story too well known
to repeat here. Even the smaller snowy egret is a common
bird of roadside ditches in Florida, and now once more
nests as far north as New Jersey. The same society also
does invaluable work in guarding breeding rookeries of
many spectacular southern water-birds, egrets, herons, ibis,
cranes, and spoonbill, the majority of which have shown
a most gratifying increase.

On the other hand the great wild-life refuge program
of the United States Fish and Wild Life Service deserves
chief credit for building up the supply of waterfowl. A
four hundred per cent increase in twenty years is an outstanding achievement. These refuges benefit many other
birds of special interest in addition, such as turkeys and
grouse of several kinds; certain spectacular shore-birds,
the avocet, marbled godwit, and long billed curlew, Frank-

lin's gull, and the white pelican, to mention only a few.

At the moment the whooping crane and ivory-billed woodpecker seem doomed to extinction, and the California condor shows no substantial increase. The four kites are not even holding their own. Most of our rails, larger hawks, and owls are steadily decreasing, though in no case can any of the better-known species of wide range be called rare. In these cases in particular the field ornithologist is in a "middle of the road" position. He knows that the claim of one group of selfish interests, that "there are just as many as ever," is absolutely untrue. He knows equally well that the long lists which have been published of so-called vanishing North American birds are a figment of the heated imagination of fanatical protectionists, whose opinions are based primarily on a woeful lack of sufficiently wide field experience. Needless to say, both extremes do real harm to the progress of conservation and wild-life management, now recognized scientific studies, a branch of biology.

Finally, the field ornithologist is the only person interested in the decrease of certain North American birds which are not of interest to the sportsman, and whose cause has never been taken up by anybody. The extreme rarity of the eastern harlequin duck was probably due to overshooting decades ago, but it has ceased to figure as a game bird. Biologically the most interesting cases are those where no cause whatever can be alleged. Outstanding examples in the eastern States are the nighthawk and yellow-throated vireo. If anyone wished to take a trip to find the beautiful and distinct Bachman's warbler, regardless of time, trouble, or expense, there is not a single locality in North America where he could be directed to go and be certain of success.

REFERENCE

1. MURPHY, ROBERT CUSHMAN. Oceanic Birds of South America. New York: American Museum of Natural History, 1936. See vol. 1, p. 511.

CHAPTER IV

MIGRATION: CAUSES AND ORIGIN

BIRD migration is, perhaps, the most distinctive phase of bird-life, and in its greatest development offers one of the most remarkable phenomena in the animal kingdom.

The word "migration" is not used of birds in the sense of the straight dictionary definition. Human beings, for instance, have been migrating long before the dawn of exact history, but in most cases they have occupied new territory and never intended or attempted to return from whence they came.

In the modern historical period, there are very few cases of this sort in birds. One of those which is absolutely authenticated is that of a northern finch, the crossbill of the northern conifer forests, which is subject to irruptions in various directions upon the failure of its food supply of cones. On numerous occasions the crossbills from northern Europe have invaded western Europe; they have even crossed the Irish Sea to Ireland. There was a particularly great flight in the year 1888, and so many crossbills reached Ireland that some have remained there ever since. They have increased in numbers, and are now permanent residents in the great majority of the counties of

Ireland, where it is positively known that they were not resident prior to the year 1888.

But, coming back to the question of migration in birds, we usually understand an additional element of periodicity. For one set of reasons or another, birds leave their breeding areas, travel varying distances to winter quarters, and return the following year to the same breeding areas, on a remarkably exact time schedule. A human analogy, perhaps, is the migration of the Bakhtiari tribe in Persia, which was filmed some twenty years ago.

By migration in birds, it is usually still further understood that in its greatest development northern birds fly south to escape winter, and hence a seasonal change of climate is required. Actually, this state of affairs is true of only about fifteen per cent of all birds on earth, and such a generalization conceals many facts of interest and significance.

Any attempt, therefore, to define bird migration involves consideration of other English words, such as wandering, vagrancy, nomads, etc. We now know enough about the movements of birds to be able to state positively that some birds at least exhibit every conceivable transition between strictly resident species and the opposite extreme, the shore-birds, some of which quite unnecessarily rush from one end of the world to the other twice each year on a reasonably exact timetable. Any definition of migration, consequently, involves the selection of a purely arbitrary criterion.

It is not until we study the elementary and simple types

of migration that we get a clue to the multiple factors which originated it.

Science advances by the discovery of a certain series of facts, and then a theory is evolved to account for them. If the theory is good, all the facts known at that time are properly accounted for; but if the theory is bad, or if new facts develop which cannot be reconciled with the old theory, a second theory is formulated. The proponents of these two theories debate the matter, each urging the claims for his own theory, and it is not until the sound and fury has died down that it occurs to anybody that both theories are required to explain different sets of facts. This has been very much the case with bird migration: in the last hundred years, five or six different theories have been evolved to account for its origin. The probabilities are that not one single one of them is correct for all types of bird migration, but the chances are equally good that all of them are correct for the migration of some birds.

Several different types of bird migration can be cited to prove that no dividing line exists between no migration at all and that of maximum extent.

In the first place, there is a category which might be called migration without periodicity, and there are at least three types of this sort.

The first type is possibly caused by a surplus population. This is inferred in birds, but has not as yet been really proved. A familiar and famous case in mammals is that of the arctic lemmings, which, after a favorable number of years, become so abundant in one section or another of arctic Europe that they irrupt southward, eastward, or westward. These wandering lemmings encounter all sorts and kinds of disasters and dangers, and probably the great majority of them never return where they came from and perish miserably. But in this way the surplus population is reduced greatly.

In the arid steppes of Asia there is a peculiar bird known as Pallas's sand-grouse, which looks something like a hybrid between a pigeon and a quail. This sand-grouse is given to periodic irruptions of the same sort as the lemmings; at long and irregular intervals it has invaded Europe in great numbers; it has even penetrated as far as the British Isles. There was a great visitation of sand-grouse to Europe in the year 1863; and there was an even greater one in 1888. So many sand-grouse reached Great Britain and settled down there, apparently as permanent residents, that a Special Act of Parliament was passed to protect them on the chance that they might remain and become regular members of the bird population, but they did not, and in the course of time all these European sand-grouse died or disappeared. It is not known whether any of them ever returned to their native steppes in Asia or not.

I wish to point out that there is no final proof in this case that the original cause was a surplus population, owing to the very simple fact that there were no resident ornithologists in the Asiatic steppes, so no one could testify against the fact that the departure of the sand-grouse was due to a failure of their normal food supply.

This leads us, naturally, to the second type of migration without periodicity, where we positively know that the migration of the birds is brought about by a failure of their food supply. Outstanding cases of this sort in the New World are the goshawk and the snowy owl in the Arctic. Their southward flights into the United States are known to be correlated with years of scarcity of their food supply of ptarmigan, hares, and voles, and have nothing to do with a cold winter.

In the case of the crossbills, I have just mentioned how they desert a breeding territory where they may have been residents for a considerable stretch of years, upon the exhaustion of the supply of cones. Botanists now tell us that the conifers fruit irregularly and erratically, and for one set of reasons or another there will be a period of years when the spruce or hemlock in a given forest will not bear any cones. Food, consequently, is positively the factor that causes the migration of these birds, and not cold weather, to which they are indifferent.

There is a group of high arctic seafowl of various species, which move around the Pole east and west, looking for unfrozen stretches of ocean. They never move south, as far as our records go. This is particularly true of certain seabirds which nest on the islands north of Siberia, where the Arctic Ocean freezes solid every winter. Some of these birds move east to the warmer waters of the Arctic Ocean north and west of Alaska, and a smaller number of them move west to northern Europe, where, in extreme Arctic Russia and Finland, they again strike a stretch of unfrozen and open ocean all winter long (which the United Nations have found exceedingly useful in the last two or three years in bringing much-needed war supplies to Russia).

A third category of migration without periodicity is found in what may be called the nomad group of birds in the arid continent of Australia. Here, the birds depend for their food supply upon rains, which are exceedingly erratic and irregular. In that portion of the continent of Australia which lies between the severe central deserts and the well-watered coast ranges of eastern Australia, there are numerous parts of the continent where it may not rain for two years in succession. Then the rains come, and sometimes they may be abundant. When the rains do come in any particular district, the trees flower and fruit, and various groups of birds like parrots, cockatoos, and honeyeaters, which live on the flowers and fruits of trees and other plants, suddenly arrive in this district apparently from any one of the four points of the compass, and they remain for such time as the food supply lasts. If the rains have been abundant, the trees and flowers fruit in quantity; so the birds may remain for several months, and even a year and a half or two years. Then, as the country dries up once more, the flowers and fruit disappear, the trees go into a protracted resting period, and these birds wander off to some other part of Australia, presumably where it has rained and where they can find the flowers and fruits that they require.

All we have to do in a case such as this is to imagine a climatic change taking place in which these rains become seasonal rather than erratic and irregular, and this is all that would be required, obviously, for a regular and periodic migration of the birds to develop.

We now come to a category which may be called migration with some periodicity, but there is no distinctly separate summer and winter range, or, to speak more correctly, no separate breeding and non-breeding range.

For instance, let us consider the resident birds, so called, in the tropics. It is possibly true that some birds in the tropics are so extremely sedentary that they may never move more than a mile or two from where they were hatched, but in no case has any such lack of movement been proved as yet in tropical birds, owing to the fact that no banding experiments to amount to anything have as yet been undertaken. But we do know that with the great majority of the so-called resident birds in the tropics, they have a favorite and a definite breeding territory or place, and at the conclusion of the breeding season they wander off and disappear from this breeding territory; for our present purposes, it makes no difference just how far they may go. But at the end of eleven months, on a stated schedule, back they come to their favorite breeding area in the forest, and next year's breeding season takes place.

Dr. Chapman, the great ornithologist of New York, made a close study of some giant oropendolas on a little island in Lake Gatun in the Canal Zone. He was unable to discover just how far away these oropendolas went, but he determined that they did leave, that they disappeared completely, and that the following year, within a week, they came back to the ancestral nesting tree, repaired their gigantic hang-nests, and commenced the new breeding season.

In the case of certain birds with highly specialized or limited feeding habits, it is only common sense to infer that they are forced to travel considerable distances for their food. The little violet and yellow euphonia tanagers, for instance, in tropical America, feed only on mistletoe berries, and they are, consequently, forced to travel long distances in the course of a year to find an adequate supply of these parasites in fruit. Hummingbirds give a further and still more remarkable illustration of restricted feeding habits. There are many hummingbirds in tropical America, chiefly in the Andes, that are, so far, birds of mystery in the sense that they are only known from one general locality, or even the slope of one mountain, where they feed on one flower only, and they stay there only for the month when that flower is in bloom. For the rest of the eleven months of the year, in a great many cases, we have not the faintest idea where they go or what becomes of them. There is a little emerald green and white hummingbird, known as *Agyrtria boucardi*, which was formerly thought to be one of the rarest and least known of Central American birds. It was originally collected in 1865 in a mangrove swamp on the west coast of Costa Rica. It was scarcely seen or heard of again until the year 1895, when a professional collector, revisiting these coastal mangrove swamps on the Pacific side of the country, found this hummingbird in great abundance, feeding on the flowers of a certain white morning-glory that was climbing over the trees. In the years which have elapsed since then, anyone who goes to the Pacific mangrove swamps in the proper month when this morning-glory is in bloom will have no difficulty in finding this hummingbird; but eighty years after its discovery we still have no idea what becomes of it for that part of the year when this morning-glory is not in bloom in the mangrove swamps. All that we do know is that it is not there. It should be clear, therefore, that the degree of wandering of these so-called resident birds can merely be a question of the type of their food supply. All return to their favorite breeding territory at a stated, annual breeding period. Here again, all that is required is the development of some seasonal regularity in the appearance of their favorite food for a periodic migration to develop.

Coming, now, to sedentary birds in North America, or any north temperate climate, again we find exactly the same principle, that the degree of territory wandered over is largely a question of the type of food supply. Chickadees, many of which are non-migratory and strictly resident throughout the year in eastern Massachusetts, do not have to travel very far to find enough insects' eggs and various other things of that sort, which constitute their food. Grouse require more territory and often wander quite a bit in fall to find a wintering ground with an adequate food supply.

Birds like the golden eagle and the great horned owl, with carnivorous habits, require a very large territory indeed to support an adequate food supply. Consequently, horned owls are few and far between, especially in the more settled or disturbed parts of the United States. A pair of eagles require many, many square miles of territory to support themselves and to raise a family in the course of the year.

Many winter sea-birds require mussels or fish as their food. The degree to which they wander southward in winter depends entirely upon whether the ocean or salt water bays and estuaries freeze or not. Certain land-birds are also affected in this way.

Here in Massachusetts there are occasional visits by a northern population of bald eagles, breeding probably much farther north than those nesting in New England. They are perhaps less migratory than our New England breeding population, which goes south and sometimes quite a distance south in the winter. The eagles of this northern population tend to go to the coast, where they live on crippled or dying ducks and fish in the estuaries along the coast of Maine. Should a particularly severe cold spell arrive and these estuaries freeze over, we will have a midwinter invasion of these northern eagles. They will be relatively abundant in Newburyport Harbor after a severe zero spell in late December or in January and, on exceptional occasions, such a winter invasion of eagles even reaches the milder climate of Cape Cod. The moment, however, that a thaw takes place, and the ice goes out of these coastal estuaries, the eagles disappear and presumably wander back north where they came from.

In many so-called resident birds in North America, there is an interesting type of post-breeding dispersal, which we are just beginning to study properly, thanks to the valuable aid of banding. The young of the year wander extensively for the first few months of their lives, and in this way populations are exchanged and very occasionally the range of the bird is extended. There are numerous returns of banded herons, gulls, ducks, and other birds, which show that the young birds of the year go east, north, west, and south from their breeding territory. A plotting of the returns of these banded birds looks like a sunburst superimposed on the map of the North American continent.

An interesting case of range extension is furnished by the barn owl, a supposedly non-migratory bird. The adult nesting pair is usually resident, but the young barn owls, when fledged, wander off in every direction. Some wander off to points 200 to 400 miles north of the regular breeding range of the species. The majority of these birds perish, or perhaps those that don't perish in the normal course of events turn southward with the arrival of severe winter conditions, and nothing comes of their wandering. But recently a pair of barn owls actually came together and nested in Cambridge, Massachusetts, constituting a notable northerly breeding record, and, even more surprisingly, the barn owls returned and nested in Cambridge the following year! The mockingbird and the Carolina wren, too, are constantly wandering north of their normal breeding range, and occasional pairs consequently nest well north of it.

The third and final kind of migration is called periodic migration, where the breeding range and the non-breeding or winter range are very distinct areas separated by a greater or less distance, and the journeys to and fro are performed with remarkable precision within regular dates.

We may again begin with the tropics, where eighty-five per cent of all birds are found. Tropical birds have long been written up as strictly resident, compared to birds in north temperate regions, and while some of this may well be true, as times goes on and we learn more and more about tropical birds, it becomes increasingly evident that there is more migration than was formerly supposed.

First, there is migration that is caused by periodic variations in the rainy season. The best example of this is in Africa, where in the west and central parts of the continent there is a great belt of equatorial humid rain forest. On either side of this belt of Congo rain forest there are broad areas of savanna and grassland which, in turn, merge still farther north and south into deserts—the great Sahara Desert to the north and the Kalahari Desert in South Africa. The seasons in these two belts of savannas are reversed, as they are on different sides of the equator, and consequently the rainy season in the northern savanna belt is at the diametrical opposite half of the year from the rainy season in the southern savanna belt. Some of these savanna birds migrate from the northern belt to the southern belt and vice versa. They fly across the equatorial rain forest, a country which they do not like, and spend the dry season in the rainy season of the opposite savanna belt. This is a clear case, therefore, of a correlation between migratory habits and a rainy season, and has nothing whatever to do with temperature. So far as I know, there is no explanation of why these birds breed only in one savanna belt rather than the other.

In South America, we have just begun to discover that the same situation exists to a certain extent. There are certain flycatchers in central and southern Brazil which nest there in the rainy season, and at the approach of the dry season depart northward and winter in the humid Amazon Valley. The fork-tailed flycatcher is a cousin of our North American scissor-tailed flycatcher, with a slate-gray and white body and a black cap, but it has the same tremendously long forked tail. The fork-tailed flycatchers of the savannas of central Brazil migrate across the Amazon Valley to the savannas of the coastal Guianas, and when I was in British Guiana a few years ago in the third week in March they were arriving from the south daily in numbers. With them were North American barn swallows at the beginning of their great journey across South America and across the Caribbean Sea to the northern United States. The flycatchers and barn swallows were flying north over the Guiana savannas together, though they were bound for totally different places, and their reasons for migrating and the causes back of it were quite different.

There are, finally, in the New World tropics a certain number of cases of migratory birds where no present-day cause or factors can be alleged. There is a close relative of the red-eyed vireo, for instance, in Central America, called the yellow-green vireo, which has occurred accidentally in the United States in southern Texas. The yellow-green vireo is just as migratory as its more northerly cousin. The first birds arrive in northern Central America in late March, and the bulk of the population arrives the first week in April. But if we go as far south as Panama, the yellow-green vireo proves to be resident throughout the year. The only difference to be noticed is that Panama is in the humid tropics, with an evergreen, deciduous forest throughout the year, and in northern Central America where the yellow-green vireo is a summer resident only, it arrives at the beginning of the rainy season when the trees come into leaf and flower.

In the West Indies, there are still other migratory tropical birds, like the martins and the gray kingbird, which leave the region at the end of the breeding season, migrate south-ward various distances—in certain cases to the Amazon Valley in South America—and return north to Cuba, Ja-maica, and the other islands of the Greater Antilles on a regular schedule the following spring. Here it is impossible to allege that any failure of food supply has taken place. There are numerous flycatchers, for instance, that spend the entire year in the West Indies, and it is obvious that there are plenty of insects all the year round. Why, then, does the gray kingbird migrate southward? As a matter of fact, we do not know the answer to this question, and the only conceivable theory that has ever been advanced is that these birds were migratory prior to the Ice Age, that they were forced south to their present range by the refrigera-tion of the climate, and that they retain a habit which is no longer necessary. While this theory may appear intellectually attractive, there is no way in which its correctness can ever be proved!

To sum up, the conclusion from all these facts is that some birds, at least, in the tropics, are migratory, and others are migratory at its northern limits. For all we know to the contrary, some birds may have been—nay, must have been—migratory in past geological time, long before any Ice Age, when warmer climates brought tropical temperatures much farther north than now.

Turning our attention for a moment to south temperate regions, we find migration poorly developed because of several climatic and topographic factors. In southern South America there are a mere handful of birds which are summer residents in Argentina and Patagonia and which retire northward to the tropics at the approach of winter.

An outstanding topographic feature of southern South America is that the continent is rapidly narrowing to an acute triangle at Cape Horn. In the second place, climatically, while it is cold and disagreeable in Patagonia there is relatively little contrast between summer and winter. The winter is relatively mild compared to similar north temperate latitudes, and there is a very cold and disagreeable summer instead of a hot one. In north temperate latitudes, 75 per cent of the world is land, and in south temperate latitudes, 90 per cent of the world's surface is open ocean.

Turning to periodic migration in north temperate latitudes, it should be explained that North American birds are divisible into two great groups of families and genera, those of northern or Old World origin and relationships, and others now, at least, of primarily tropical affinities and distribution. It so happens that, to a striking degree, the migratory members of these two groups have significant differences in their type of migration. The birds of northern origin migrate south because of sharp seasonal changes in climate and the resultant failure of their food supply. Contrary to the popular belief, temperature is almost never a primary factor with birds but *is purely secondary*. This point is of the greatest biological importance, and should never be forgotten. Of all living creatures, birds are the *most perfectly adapted* to withstand extremes of temperatures. If we compare birds to certain mammals, frogs, or insects, the last simply cannot survive cold winter weather. The mammals and frogs hibernate. The insects perish, but their eggs hatch out the following spring. Most birds, if they get enough to eat, can survive the temperatures of a northern winter, whether they have ever previously experienced them or not. They go south because the falling temperatures remove their food supply and not because of falling temperatures.

Tropical birds such as parrots and macaws in captivity readily become adapted to our cool northern climate and can be kept outdoors much of the year. There are a few cases on record of insectivorous birds which normally winter in the tropics having survived well into the northern winter. I recall a mourning warbler found in February at Waltham, Massachusetts; the ground was deeply covered with snow and the temperature fell to 10 degrees every night; it seemed incredible that it had survived so long, and it is difficult to imagine what it found to eat. There are now countless records of warblers and orioles found in December and January in the northern States. In every case it must be remembered that there was *something wrong with every one* of these birds to begin with, or they would have reached Central America by October at the latest. It is gratuitous to suppose that the winter cold was solely responsible for their deaths.

Under exceptional conditions, where an adequate food supply is miraculously available, such birds have survived the entire winter. Every year teal and wood ducks or coot join our city park mallards and black ducks and spend a happy winter on handouts of corn and bread. Supplies of suet at feeding stations have kept orioles, rose-breasted grosbeaks, orange-crowned warblers, dickcissels, and mockingbirds alive all winter in Massachusetts, and they have survived temperatures of 20 degrees below zero. Human beings cannot compete with birds in their ability to withstand low temperatures. To think of birds as "delicate little creatures" is a delusion.

It consequently follows that the journeys this group of birds of northern origin perform are mostly short, and they proceed no farther south than necessary to insure an adequate food supply in winter. In some cases they do not go south far enough, and they starve to death in large numbers in severe cold waves in the southern states. In 1895, for instance, 50 per cent of the bluebirds wintering in the southern states starved as the result of an extraordinary cold wave, and in the winter of 1940 the tree swallows in Florida perished in countless thousands because of an extraordinary freeze south to the Keys, which lasted for three days in succession before the thaw, and eliminated their flying insect food. In no single species of this northern group of birds does the entire population enter the tropics, and in only a few cases do a few individuals reach the tropics. Examples are the blue-winged teal, some of which reach Central America every winter. Some Savannah sparrows winter as far north as the coast of Massachusetts, but I have, myself, found them on the coast of Yucatan, which is certainly in the tropics.

The 150 or more species concerned may be divided into two groups, which furnish ideal examples of my point. The first group are the very earliest spring migrants known; birds like the Canada goose, the pintail, the crow, the robin, and the blackbirds, whose food supply is rendered available by the first spring thaws.

An enormous amount of observation and data prove that these birds move north on the isotherm of 35 degrees Fahrenheit, and the date of their arrival at tree line in northwestern Alaska in any one year can be predicted with absolute accuracy. They will not get there until the first spring thaws have taken place, and until the average temperature has reached 35 degrees. The migration of these birds lacks periodicity only in the sense that the commencement of spring can vary as much as a month from one year to the next. In Massachusetts, for instance, we get the early spring birds in late February in occasional years; in particularly backward years we will not get the beginnings of spring until late March. In fall, the departure southward of this group of birds is governed by exactly the same factors in reverse, with an equal variation in date, owing to the variation in the arrival of winter conditions.

The second group of birds of northern origin is a little later than the first; in Massachusetts, from late March to mid-April. The junco and the hermit thrush, for instance, differ in migratory habits from the first group only in one respect, and that is that the fall migration southward begins for a few individuals earlier than necessary, in the sense that cold weather has not terminated the food supply of these individuals. A very few individuals of the junco always reach eastern Massachusetts by the third week in September, whereas it is not until the end of October that the main flight of juncos from the north arrives. No one can claim that the arrival of these early September juncos was caused by the termination of their food supply on their breeding grounds in northern New England, and in this respect they furnish an apparent exception to the general principle that food is more important than temperature. On the other hand, these few individuals are probably motivated by other factors than temperature.

The second great group of migratory birds, of Neotropical origin or affinities, are insectivorous. Their journey north is conditioned by the trees coming into full leaf. In Massachusetts, consequently, their main arrival or passage through the State takes place between the 10th and the 25th of May. But utterly different is their fall migration.

Allan D. Cruickshank

SNOW GEESE

On their California winter quarters

Allan D. Cruickshank

PINTAIL DUCKS ON MIGRATION

They start south immediately after the nesting season and the post-nuptial molt, leaving the country when the temperature is at its maximum, when the vegetation is at its maximum luxuriance, and when insects are at their maximum abundance. Only one per cent in the way of stragglers lingers to be actually driven out by the killing frosts in late September or early October, which cause the falling of the leaves and the final disappearance of insect life.

The great majority of species and individuals go much farther south than necessary for food and shelter. No one can seriously claim that a bird like the chestnut-sided warbler has to go to equatorial latitudes in South America, whereas half of our North American warblers manage to get along very well in the winter in northern Central America. The suggestion has been made, consequently, that these birds are returning to the general area of their ancestral home. The present northern breeding ranges have been acquired by aggressive types since the Ice Age, as a means of conquering or overcoming the overwhelming competition and congestion in the tropics. If, further, we make the permissible postulate that some of them, at least, were partially migratory in preglacial time in tropical or subtropical climates in North America, it is easily seen that the profound climatic vicissitudes through which they passed in Pleistocene time must more than have served to confirm them in their present remarkable migratory habits and routes.

There is a final and to me the most interesting case of periodic migration, where enormous distances separate the breeding and the winter range. An outstanding illustration in the northern hemisphere, which I have already mentioned, are certain arctic nesting shore-birds. They are arctic only in the sense that they nest north of the Arctic Circle and they go to southern South America in winter. The sanderling, for instance, has the greatest winter range of any bird in the New World. Every year some winter on Cape Cod, Massachusetts, while some go to Cape Horn, and there is no telling why some sanderlings winter so far north, or why some sanderlings go so far south. The wandering tatlers of Alaska, the Pacific godwit, the turnstone, and the bristle-thighed curlew are found in winter on every single remote island and coral reef in the vast expanse of the Pacific Ocean, south to Australia and New Zealand. They cover, therefore, the whole of Polynesia and Melanesia in their migrations.

Even more remarkable are certain of our New World shore-birds, whose winter ranges and migration routes are definitely known. The upland plover makes a nonstop flight across the tropics and winters in the Argentine, Paraguay, and Bolivia. But some upland plover get lost, I suppose, just like our smaller land-birds. Every year there are what we call accidental stragglers, which get to the wrong side of the continent, or which go east or west by mistake instead of going south. They are defective or unhealthy birds in one way or another, and I suppose that some shore-birds also are defective and get lost. The result is that they turn up in almost incredible parts of the world, so remarkable are their powers of flight and so inexhaustible their energy.

The upland plover has occurred several times in England, in France, in Italy, and in the continent of Australia!

The Hudsonian godwit also winters in southern South America, and has been flying from Massachusetts to Argentina in one nonstop flight every year, from century to century, and from millennium to millennium. Here is a shore-bird with so fixed a migration route that it has only once occurred in Alaska, and only three or four individuals have ever straggled to the Pacific Coast of the United States in the fall migration. So how do you propose to explain the fact that the Hudsonian godwit is an occasional fall visitor to New Zealand, 7,000 miles southwest of its normal route, the last occurrence being in September, 1943? I cannot explain it, but I cite it as an illustration of extraordinary and remarkable powers in bird flight. As far as our knowledge of these shore-birds is concerned, we have no clue as to the reason for their tremendous migration; we do not know what caused it, or whether it is of any necessity or advantage to the species biologically in modern times or not.

The most spectacular migration of all on earth is unfortunately the one that is the least known, and has been the least mentioned in popular accounts of the migration of birds, and I have, consequently, deliberately left it to the last. This is the migration of certain tropical and south temperate pelagic sea-birds. These birds arrive on their breeding islands within a few days of the same period in every year. They wander over the seas of the whole world, or at least the tropical seas of the whole world, for ten months of the year, and it is nothing to them to be eight and nine thousand miles away from their breeding grounds in the middle of their non-breeding season. The sooty tern, the noddy, the booby, and the Audubon's shearwater nest in colonies in the West Indies; for ten months of the year they wander over the tropical Atlantic but return to their rookeries in the various bird islands in the West Indies and the Dry Tortugas of Florida approximately the same week of every year. The yellow-billed tropic bird has a far northern and outlying station on the island of Bermuda in the central Atlantic, and the first birds always arrive in Bermuda the last three or four days of March.

The sooty shearwater is a bird which breeds on small islands off the coasts of New Zealand and Cape Horn. At the conclusion of the breeding season these shearwaters desert this territory completely and, crossing the tropical latitudes of the ocean with great rapidity and apparently without stopping to feed, they spread over the oceans of the northern hemisphere, north to the Aleutian Islands in the Pacific and to Greenland in the Atlantic Ocean. What is more, they travel on their migrations in great flocks, and a million and a quarter birds have been counted passing north up the coast of California in the course of one day.

The more we learn about the famous wandering albatross, the more extraordinary and spectacular are its powers of flight. Feeble indeed, by comparison, are most of the records that have been published, and the banding returns that have accumulated in recent years in the north temperate zone, which have been widely publicized as examples of speed or distance of flight. A wandering albatross banded on the Kerguelen Islands in the Antarctic, south of Africa, was shot twelve days later 3,150 miles away. Another banded wandering albatross has been recovered 6,000 miles from its breeding islands. Ornithologists who have studied the matter have every reason to believe that some of these albatrosses and shearwaters of the south temperate oceans go around the world in the latitudes of the "roaring forties," where the winds and the great seas go around the world.

Finally, there is the slender-billed shearwater, the famous mutton bird of Australia, a close cousin of our own sooty shearwater, which nests on Green Island in Bass Straits between South Australia and Tasmania, and also on Phillips Island, off the coast of Victoria. The flock of these shearwaters approaching their breeding grounds on Green Island in the year 1839 was estimated by John Gould to contain one hundred and fifty million birds. Their arrival on their breeding grounds is one of the most spectacular events in natural history. Let us say it is Monday in a certain week in November; three or four mutton birds arrive on Green Island; a few more on Tuesday; perhaps several hundred birds during Wednesday. But, on Wednesday night, at eight P.M., the remaining millions arrive. This migration is so definite that the breeding population on Phillips Island off the coast of Victoria will arrive at seven forty-five P.M. on the 23rd of November, and the breeding population on Green Island will arrive at eight P.M. on November 24th!

In spite of the fact that the young are used commercially for food, oil, and fat, and that a quarter of a million young per year are taken off both of these breeding islands, no appreciable diminution in their numbers was recorded between 1839 and 1910. These shearwaters spread over the whole northern Pacific; in the non-breeding season they occur in some numbers off the coast of Japan and the western United States, and some reach the coast of Alaska and the Aleutian Islands, but no matter how many thousands of miles they travel or wander during the course of the year, they may return to their breeding islands the same week, even the same day and the same quarter-hour. This is sufficiently spectacular, even though there is no truth in the popular belief that all arrive the *same day* of the month *every* year, and lay their eggs on the same day.

REFERENCES

1. GRISCOM, LUDLOW. A Monographic Study of the Red Crossbill. *Proceedings of the Boston Society of Natural History*, vol. 41, no. 5, Jan. 1937, p. 127.
2. MURPHY, ROBERT CUSHMAN. Oceanic Birds of South America. New York: American Museum of Natural History, 1936. See vol. 1, p. 546.
3. GOULD, JOHN. Birds of Australia. London, 1865. See vol. 2, pp. 459–464.
4. ANONYMOUS. The Arrival of the Mutton-Birds—A Remarkable Sight. *Emu*, vol. 24, April 1925, pp. 305–306.
5. LEWIS, F. Observations on the Mutton-birds of Phillips Island, Victoria. *Emu*, vol. 24, April 1925, pp. 86–90.

CHAPTER V

MIGRATION: FACTORS AND ROUTES

It requires little imagination to realize that while migration is an important part in the life of many birds, it is dangerous, in the sense that a large number of individuals of the species concerned perish annually because of it. It certainly consumes time and energy, and the question arises: Where does this energy come from, what motivates it, and what is the physiology involved?

One outstanding fact, true of all birds, is that migration is closely connected with the advent of the breeding season. In birds, in marked contradistinction to mammals, the reproductive organs are internal with an annual cycle; the breeding season takes place only once a year, and these organs in both sexes decrease to a relatively minute size in the winter half of the year when, in some cases, they are so small that it takes very careful dissection and a hand lens to tell one sex from the other. At the height of the breeding season, however, they enlarge to enormous proportions, in certain cases twenty-five to thirty times their size in the non-breeding season, when they fill a very respectable percentage of the body cavity. The advent of the breeding season means that the reproductive organs begin to swell, and the "spring" migration of most birds is so controlled that they arrive on their breeding grounds at the time of the year when they are, in fact, ready to breed. It is consequently believed that the secretion into the system of the sex hormones plays an important part in the energy needed to perform the migration.)

In the northern hemisphere it was noted a century ago that the migration of birds northward to their breeding grounds was attended with a rise of temperature, passing from the cold temperatures of winter to warm summer temperatures, and it was, consequently, supposed that this rise in temperature was another factor that gave the birds their impulse to migrate northward.

A relatively recent discovery, due to the brilliant experiments of Professor Rowan in Alberta, has been fondly believed in popular write-ups to solve the so-called "riddle" of migration. As a very brief summary, Professor Rowan conceived the ingenious idea of catching crows, juncos, and ducks, and keeping them in captivity during the fall and the bitter Alberta winter. He so managed things that gradually, day by day, in the middle of winter, the temperature in the rooms where these birds were kept was allowed to increase steadily, and at the same time the number of hours of light was also allowed to increase. After doing this at the wrong time of the year, so to speak, for a month or so, by killing a certain number of birds and dissecting them, he discovered that their reproductive organs had begun to enlarge, and by banding and releasing others in the bitter midwinter cold of Alberta, he discovered that many of them did, in fact, actually start migrating northward, as was proved by their recovery at various distances north of the place where they were released. These experiments proved conclusively, therefore, that a rise in temperature and *an increase in the hours of daylight* were important factors in the stimulation of these birds' reproductive organs.

Now, while I yield to none in my admiration for these experiments and the interesting light that they have cast on this problem, it must be admitted that experimental research in this connection is still in its infancy, and I, consequently, offer the following comments on the difficulty and danger of drawing too broad conclusions from too few data, which, incidentally, Professor Rowan did not do.

To comment on temperature first. In the last chapter I pointed out that the spring migration northward of the robin, among other birds, followed the isotherm of 35 degrees. As far as the robin is concerned, therefore, there isn't any rise in temperature for the whole two months that it takes it to get from the southern states to tree line in northwestern Alaska; the temperature is always at an average of 35 degrees. Moreover, in the case of very early migrants, like the robins, very little increase in temperature, if any, has taken place, because the great majority of individuals winter in the southern states, where the normal mean winter temperature is at approximately 35 degrees anyhow.

But, when all is said and done, this question of rise of temperature and increase of daylight hours can only apply to those birds which winter in temperate climates, and which belong to the great group of migrating birds of boreal or Old World origin. We notice in passing that as the great majority of birds in this group move northward, their spring molt is concluded and they are in song.

The same principles cannot possibly apply, however, to those insect-eating species which winter in the tropics. It is remarkable how people have forgotten that the great majority of our migrating birds do winter in the tropics, and that often one-half of the total distance traversed by them in their journey from their winter quarters to their breeding ground has, in fact, taken place in the tropics.

Consider, for instance, those birds which winter at or near the equator. Everyone surely appreciates that there is no change in the length of daylight hours throughout the year on the equator, nor is there the slightest change in the average temperature throughout the year. What, then, starts these birds northward in mid-March? They pass through Panama in late March and the first week in April. They are passing through northern Central America in mid-April, and they pass through southern Texas in maximum numbers between April 20 and 25. In western Panama, where I studied these migrants with care, they are not in song, the spring molt has not begun, and those birds which were collected showed little or no enlargement in their reproductive organs. Even in southern Texas, when half, at least, of their journey northward is concluded, they have not yet become sufficiently physiologically advanced to be in song, the swarms of migrants are silent, and in many cases the spring molt is not completed.

Furthermore, it is quite obvious that as these tropical

wintering birds move northward the average temperature is, for them, *decreasing*. No reader can seriously believe that the average temperature around Boston on or about the 10th of May even remotely resembles the tropical temperatures to which these birds have been accustomed for at least the six preceding months! With those birds which spend their entire lives in the tropics, and also migrate, no factors are yet known which produce the physiological development resulting in the onset of the breeding season, and this is still a matter for research in the future.

If we consider the highly migratory North American shore-birds that breed in the Arctic and winter in southern South America, the situation becomes even more paradoxical, because they leave southern South America, northbound, in March and April. This is the middle of fall in south temperate climates, and consequently the number of daylight hours and the temperature have been steadily *decreasing* for some time. The same situation is true in reverse in the case of the Antarctic sea-birds that go to the northern hemisphere in the summer. Whatever impulse starts them on their 9,000-mile journey to their breeding grounds in south temperate latitudes, it certainly is not any increase in temperature or in daylight hours, because the diametrical opposite has been taking place for some time. We have here, consequently, a vivid illustration of where more research and experiment are badly needed in ornithology, and where a current theory does not fit all the known facts.

There are further points of interest about those birds

which winter in the tropics. Whatever may prove to be the factors which bring them north to the United States, let us see by what routes they reach the United States and how they move northward. There are four principal routes, which have been well known for years.

A great group of summer residents in the western United States winter in the tableland of Mexico and Guatemala and few or no individuals go any farther south. These birds migrate north through the Rockies and the Pacific coastal plain. Most of this route is highly mountainous and the topography is exceedingly jumbled. Very different climates occur on the summits of the mountains, as compared with their bases. A relatively small number of species is involved. Some hop from one zone to another, from mountain peak to mountain peak, and do not bother with the adjacent lowlands. Other birds move northward through the lowlands, and dodge the mountains as best they can. Consequently, the migration in the western United States is entirely devoid of those spectacular and varied features which make it so fascinating a basis for field experience and study in the east.

The climate is far more uniform on the Pacific Coast than in the east. The summer residents tend to arrive with unvarying and monotonous regularity. A colleague of mine, one of the leading ornithologists of California, has spent several springs in field work in ideal country in the coastal plain of California. He has told me how disappointing the spring migration is as regards the land-birds. There is an enormous list of permanent residents; there is a very large list of winter residents or visitors, which gradually disappears northward in spring; a relatively small list of summer residents arrives on scheduled time, and in one par-

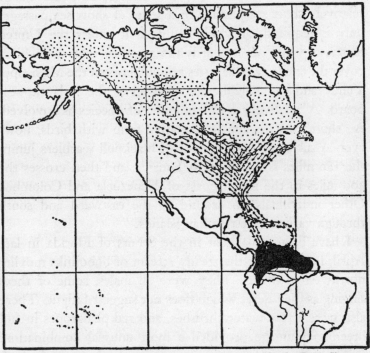

Handbook to Birds of Eastern North America, by F. M. Chapman.
D. Appleton-Century Company

MIGRATION ROUTE OF THE BLACKPOLL WARBLER

ticular spring he saw a total of twelve individuals of nine species of migrants bound for farther north than California. It must be admitted that the great majority of field observers in the east, if they got such poor returns as that for their efforts, would not undertake intensive birding for very long.

The second great route from the tropics to the United States is via the West Indies and the Florida peninsula. A relatively short sea passage or a series of short sea passages only is required, and this route, as it enters the United States, expands out towards the west, so that these birds cover the entire central states region between the Mississippi Valley and the Alleghenies, as well as the Atlantic seaboard. A relatively small number of species is involved. A "short" sea passage is a relative term with birds, however. A substantial contingent of blackpoll warblers jumps the 180 miles from Cuba to Jamaica, and then crosses the 400 miles to the north coast of Venezuela and Colombia. Other individuals go around to the eastward and south through various West Indian islands.

I have been on a boat in the Straits of Florida in late April, fascinated at the steady stream of bobolinks moving northwest in flocks. They were all males, some of them singing as they flew, which does not suggest fatigue. There also were a few water-thrushes, and red phalaropes in full breeding plumage provided a most unusual combination.

The next most important route is a land route, through Central America, up the east side of Mexico and coastal Texas, and the birds on this route fan out both westward and eastward, so that in the northern tier of states they spread across the entire country from the Atlantic seaboard to the western edge of the Great Plains. Although no sea passage is involved, there are four hundred miles of sterile, arid, and unfavorable coastal prairie, largely treeless, in northern Mexico and along the coastline of Texas. The great majority of our insectivorous and woodland song-

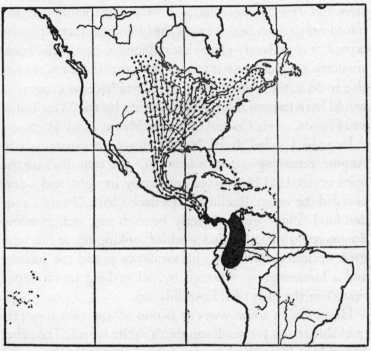

Handbook to Birds of Eastern North America, by F. M. Chapman.
D. Appleton-Century Company

MIGRATION ROUTE OF THE MOURNING WARBLER

birds do not like this country and pass over it as rapidly as possible, not stopping if they can possibly help it.

The greatest route of all is from the tip of the Yucatan peninsula across the Gulf of Mexico to the mouth of the

Mississippi River. This route also fans out, some birds reaching the United States anywhere from western Louisiana to northwestern Florida. A passage of 500–700 miles across the Gulf of Mexico is involved. From one point of view this can be regarded as a very remarkable and extraordinary route, but as far as the biological facts are concerned, it is perfectly clear that millions of small land-birds are perfectly able to do it twice each year. If they were not able to do it, they would long since have become extinct, or would have learned to go around, either by the West Indies and Florida, or via Central America, Mexico, and Texas.

In 1930 I sailed from New Orleans to Guatemala in August, returning a month later. For the two days on the open ocean, land-birds were constantly in sight, and a few boarded the vessel. Reclining in a deck-chair, I heard a sudden loud "chip" given directly beneath me, and, glancing down, saw a male hooded warbler looking up at me with great curiosity. Barn and cliff swallows passed the steamer and a hummingbird whizzed by, all making much better time than the boat could possibly do.

However, in some ways it is one of the two most remarkable routes for small songbirds in the world. The other is used by a large number of species that nest in Siberia and winter in the tropical plains of India. These birds have to fly across the gigantic ranges of the Himalayan mountains. Many years ago two Americans, Dr. and Mrs. Bullock Workman, mountaineers and explorers primarily, spent a long season in the Kashmir Himalayas, making some of the first ascents in that section of the Himalayas, and

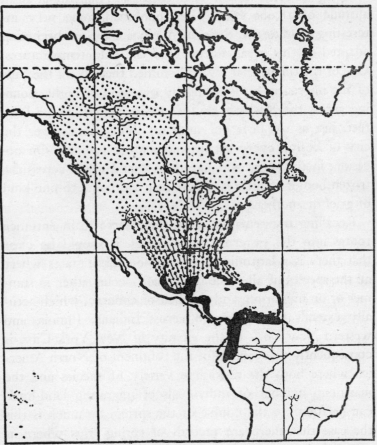

Handbook to Birds of Eastern North America, by F. M. Chapman.
D. Appleton-Century Company

MIGRATION ROUTE OF THE REDSTART

camping for some time in late August and September at an altitude of 18,000 feet. They published some very interesting studies on their own physiology in becoming adapted to this great altitude and the cold temperatures. One of the things that most astonished them were the calls of the migrating birds flying by overhead at night, pouring across the Kashmir sky at 18,000, 19,000, and 20,000 feet, just as we hear our migrants flying north over the city of Boston every spring and south every fall. On occasion, in the snow and ice, they would come across the frozen bodies of little warblers that had come to one kind of grief or another.

Recalling my remarks about these three main entrance routes into the eastern United States, it should be clear that there is a latitudinal belt in the central states where all the species of all three routes will occur either in summer or on migration, and this belt of country, which actually extends from Chicago across Indiana, Illinois, and western New York to the vicinity of New York City, is consequently that section of the continent of North America where both the maximum variety of species and the maximum number of individuals of migrating land-birds can be found in the course of the spring. So much is this the case that there are records of spring trips where as many as 160 to 170 species of birds have been seen in the course of a single day by one party.

One might readily suppose that all kinds of interesting things would occur in the southern states, where these three great streams of bird-life reach North America. As a matter of fact, the results are exceedingly disappointing to the observer. The most important reason is the lack of variation in the climate. Good birding, good results in the spring migration in the northern states, are due primarily to the exceedingly variable climate of our northern spring. A pleasant warm day or two is succeeded by a cold wave or by a northeast rainstorm, during which period the northward migration is suspended. After two or three days it warms up again, the temperature rises rapidly, the wind goes to the south, and a flood of migrants moves northward.

We northerners tend to curse the vagaries of our New England spring, and think of Florida as having an ideal spring climate. Well, so it does. One lovely day after another comes and passes; the temperature remains uniform; there are no really cold waves. There is practically no such thing as a northeast rainstorm, and the spring vegetation, the leaves on the trees, and the flowers come out slowly, gradually, and steadily. The birds move northward in exactly the same way, slowly, gradually, and steadily. Active field work in the Florida peninsula of the most strenuous kind will yield exceedingly disappointing results in the small number of migrants to be seen, compared to the northern states.

Exactly similar conditions prevail on the coast of Texas. Here it is already quite hot. The temperature goes to eighty-five, maybe to ninety, during the last half of April; the wind blows from the southeast, from the Gulf of Mexico, and is quite strong. It is a very dry climate; there is very little rain, and the treeless coastal prairies are not favorable for woodland birds, which fly right over without stopping. There are only two sets of conditions that cause them to stop. Sometimes the wind from the Gulf of Mexico blows very much more strongly. It increases markedly in velocity, and as a result the clouds come up and there may be a sharp shower one night, or in the early morning. This causes such birds as are passing over the country on that particular night to put down practically anywhere that they possibly can, so that on occasion one can obtain very astonishing results on the coastal prairies of Texas. The other factor is fog.

There is apparently one exception to these remarks. One of the most remarkable places on the whole coast of Texas is a little island in the Laguna Madre, called Green Island. It is very difficult to get there, requiring special arrangements. The country on the edge of the lagoon looks like a desert, it is so sterile and barren. The soil is a reddish-brown clay, and there is hardly any green vegetation left whatever. Out in the intensely salt lagoon is Green Island, so called because there actually is vegetation in the way of prickly, thorny, and scrubby growth of one kind or another. A less likely country for warblers, tanagers, and flycatchers I never saw! I visited the island in April, 1943, and found that a few faint trails had been hacked through the thorny scrub, which is so dense that it is absolutely impossible for a strong man to force his way through.

Theoretically, the visitor to Green Island goes there because he wishes to see the fabulous quantity and variety of

egrets, herons, and other water-birds which breed on this
island and which are guarded by an Audubon warden.
As a matter of fact, I was a great disappointment to the
hospitable warden when I visited the island. I had often
been on breeding rookeries of the southern water-birds
of the United States, and I paid scant attention to the
egrets and herons of various kinds which the warden
wanted me to see and admire. The reason why was that
I landed on the 22nd of April, and the first five minutes
that I was on this island I realized that there was one land-
bird migrant per cubic yard. They had presumably been
flying north for several hundred miles over similar country in eastern Mexico, in the state of Tamaulipas, and
this was the first green island that they had seen in some
time, and they put down there in prodigious numbers.
We saw warblers, vireos, thrushes, orioles, and flycatchers.
There were two different kinds of hummingbirds. Most of
the swallows of North America were passing by overhead
in a steady stream. Later in the day my friends and I went
to the extreme south tip of the island, and as a matter of
experiment we raised our field glasses and just looked south
over the salt waters of the lagoon. We were immediately
rewarded for doing so, because every thirty seconds one
little flock of land-bird migrants or another would fly
into the field of our glasses, and we could follow them
north until they reached Green Island and pitched down
into the bushes fifteen yards or so back of us. Hummingbirds, cuckoos, thrushes, warblers, orioles, finches, and
grosbeaks of various kinds came in every thirty seconds to

a minute during the time that we spent on the south end
of this island.

One of the most interesting things that still remains to
be done in the study of migrating birds in the United States
is for observers to go to Green Island and stay there for
the entire six or eight weeks of the spring migration, making a daily census. The report would be both interesting
and astonishing, I am sure, as to the variety of species and
the abundance of individuals that could be obtained in
that time. Moreover there are patches of green in the dune
hollows on the outer beach islands which no ornithologist
has ever visited.

On the coast of Louisiana, east of the mouth of the
Mississippi River, there is a tremendous belt of marsh, one
of the most extensive in the world, bordering the Gulf of
Mexico from Louisiana to northwest Florida. There are
several million acres of these marshes; they are several
hundred miles long, and they are sometimes forty miles
wide.

The "exhausted little birds," after their 700-mile flight
across the Gulf of Mexico, are not so exhausted after all.
They do not like these marshes, and they consequently
fly a hundred miles or so farther north before they bother
to put down in the woodland north of the coastal plain.
In the spring, at least, the mouth of the Mississippi River
in the vicinity of New Orleans is a very disappointing
place to look for a large variety and abundance of migrants.
The same situation holds good all the way around the
Gulf Coast to the east as far as northwestern Florida. I

have several times been in northwestern Florida in spring. One sees very few migrants indeed, except on the rare occasions when a cool wave causes the wind to go around to the northwest and the temperature drops ten or twenty degrees; under these circumstances, the birds coming in from over the Gulf of Mexico do not like to fly into a cold, head wind, and they put down wherever they are. Such occasions give the observer a chance to see something of the rarer spring migrants.

An opportunity for interesting and valuable field work exists, however, in the Louisiana marshes. On the Rainey Sanctuary of the Audubon Society, south of Abbeville, there are a few small trees and bushes around the building, which is on a dredged-out platform of mud. The most incidental kind of random observation has produced a list of 169 species of birds, many of them land-bird migrants. Here and there are little islands of high land in these marshes, especially along the Gulf Coast. They are covered with live oaks and are known as "cheniers." Chenier au Tigre is twenty miles south of the Rainey Sanctuary. A very few trips to this chenier indicate that at times it will literally be swarming with land-birds. The indications are that fall (mid-August to late October) would be much more spectacular than spring; at this season the birds would tend to accumulate on these coastal islands before attempting the crossing of the Gulf. There is a report of 150 Canadian warblers in one morning in late August.

After a general discussion of these main migration routes, I should like to mention the behavior of a few special birds, where detailed observation has yielded facts of some interest or novelty. Once many of them have reached the United States their rate of progress is surprisingly slow— the average number of miles per day is 16–30, a mere nothing compared to what they have just accomplished. The red-eyed vireo, for instance, arrives on the Gulf Coast the last week in March, but takes nearly six weeks to reach the northeastern states. It requires only ten more days to reach Alaska. This type of acceleration is characteristic of many species. There are several probable explanations. These birds have suddenly arrived in a climate of much cooler temperatures; the leafing out of the trees is a very slow and protracted affair in the eastern United States from south to north; in the far north, however, spring is a brief but violent burst, winter passing suddenly into summer in two to three weeks at most.

The Connecticut warbler is noted for having two different routes. In spring it appears in Florida, and moving northwestward passes up the Mississippi Valley to its breeding grounds in central Canada; in fall, however, this bird moves east and passes south through the Atlantic seaboard states. A few records indicate that its wintering grounds are in central and southern Brazil. There are practically no records in the vast intermediate area. There are, however, recent records in Louisiana, which suggest that further observation and careful search may alter the picture presented here.

An interesting case in which earlier ideas about a bird may have to be completely abandoned is that of the rare

Swainson's warbler. Among the earliest records for this bird were winter records from Cuba and Jamaica, now nearly one hundred years old. It was naturally supposed to winter in the West Indies. As a matter of fact it has never been seen or heard of again there. Many years later specimens were shot in Vera Cruz and Yucatan. Mrs. Jack Hagar in recent years has found it a regular, late March migrant in very small numbers at Rockport, Texas. It is consequently possible that it is a mere straggler to the West Indies, and that its real winter quarters are in southern Mexico.

The brown thrasher, a familiar bird, illustrates a very curious point about the Mexico–Texas route which has only been discovered in recent years by Mrs. Hagar of Rockport. It is a common summer resident in the northern states and the great majority of thrashers winter in abundance in the Gulf states and the southern states generally. It was a great surprise to discover that one population of brown thrashers uses the Texas–Mexico route, wintering apparently in Mexico where, as a matter of fact, there is practically no record of the bird. The brown thrasher is a regular and fairly common spring migrant on the coastal prairies of southern Texas, and, what is even more remarkable, it is a particularly late spring migrant. The eastern population arrives in Massachusetts about April 25, which is approximately the date that transients first appear in southern Texas!

The golden plover has been loudly heralded for two generations as being one of the champion long-distance

fliers of the world. It is supposed to have two routes, in
spring going north from its wintering ground in the pam-
pas of Argentina, Paraguay, and Brazil through the great
plains and the center of the United States to its Arctic
breeding grounds. Most of the individuals never stop between the wintering grounds and the coastal prairies of
Texas! There are hardly any records for tropical South
America and Central America in the last one hundred
years. In the fall, the golden plover used to work eastward
along the coast of the Arctic Ocean, and then proceed
down Labrador to Nova Scotia, where it rested, fattened
up, and made preparations for the 4,000-mile nonstop flight
to its wintering grounds in southern South America. Occasionally, as a result of storms and northeast gales, some
of the golden plover would be blown westward and would
alight on the coast of Massachusetts and Long Island.

This migration route was worked out many decades ago,
when the golden plover was a game bird, when it was
extensively shot throughout the United States both in
spring and fall, and as a result began to decrease rapidly in
the early nineties. Thanks to the closed season on all
shore-birds for a quarter of a century, the golden plover
was saved, so to speak, at the eleventh hour, and has been
rapidly increasing in numbers. This route has now sus-
tained very radical alterations. In the first place, the bird
is of regular occurrence, gales or no gales, on the northeast coast of the United States in the fall. It is true that
from there it makes a nonstop flight to southern South
America. It is still true that in the spring it makes a nonstop

flight from its wintering ground to the coastal prairies of Texas, where now it occurs in what seem like fabulous numbers. Just last spring, on Galveston Island, Texas, two observers saw 1,400 golden plover in the course of one morning, all in full breeding plumage, and no such number of golden plover in any one day had ever previously been reported in North America in my lifetime. But, as the bird has come back, it has ceased to use this eastern route exclusively in the autumn, and plenty of golden plover now move southward through the central states. It is a regular fall migrant on the coast of Texas.

While it would appear that the migration routes of this plover have changed, the probabilities are that the supposed change is nothing but a *return to the original normal* habits, prior to the decimation in numbers that spring market gunning in the Great Plains and constant fall shooting on the Atlantic seaboard effected. We have entirely inadequate knowledge of the golden plover's migration prior to this period.

REFERENCES

1. ROWAN, WILLIAM. Experiments in Bird Migration. *Proceedings of the Boston Society of Natural History*, 1929, pp. 39, 151–208.
2. ROWAN, W. Reversed Migration. *Proceedings of the National Academy of Science*, 1930, pp. 16, 520–525.
3. COOKE, W. W. Distribution and Migration of North American Warblers, *Bulletin 18, Biological Survey*, 1904, 152 pages.
4. COOKE, W. W. Routes of Bird Migration. *Auk*, 1905, pp. 1–11.

CHAPTER VI

DISTRIBUTION: GENERAL

EVERY living animal and plant has a definite "range." It is found, let us say, in the United States, and only occurs so far to the north, south, east, and west. Usually this range is a very limited area of the earth's surface. There are a great many factors involved, but, theoretically, the limitations of range could be explained for every living thing, if only we had complete knowledge of all the necessary details.

The distribution of birds can consequently be considered from several points of view. Beginning with the birds themselves, the exact range of every known species can be ascertained, obviously a gigantic mass of detailed facts, which does not lend itself to any general treatment. Similarly, we can approach it geographically and list the birds of Massachusetts or of any region on earth whatever, which happens to interest us. Here also no general treatment is possible.

On the other hand, all this detail can be taken for granted. The bird-life of a whole continent may be compared with that of another continent. Tropical bird-life may be contrasted with that of cold and temperate regions. It appears that climatic and geographic factors are of vital importance; deserts and mountain ranges exert great effect. There are also historical factors of considerable influence; climates have altered; the outlines of continents have changed; connections between them have taken place or been severed; the fossil record sometimes tells us that birds ranged more widely once upon a time, or originated in a part of the world where they do not occur now. All too meager are the facts, but their implications are stimulating and thought-provoking.

As regards birds, and to a large extent mammals, *historically* orders originated before families, families first appeared on earth before their present-day component genera, and genera appeared before their present-day component species.

Geographically, orders tend to be world-wide in distribution. Families and groups of genera are often limited to one or another of the great continents or one zoogeographic region, and genera and species are often characteristic of parts of continents only.

A zoogeographic region is an area of the earth's surface characterized by many peculiar families and genera, a great assemblage of mammals and birds found nowhere else. Its boundaries are usually oceans, or, if the land mass is continuous, abrupt climatic or topographic boundaries separate two peculiar assemblages. Thus the Holarctic Region includes the whole of Europe, northern Asia, North America, and North Africa. The Himalaya Mountains separate this region from the Oriental (tropical Asia, etc.).

The Sahara Desert separates the Holarctic Region from the African or Ethiopian Region. The Neotropical Region includes Central America and the West Indies as well as South America. Australia, New Zealand, and Antarctica are completely isolated.

Climatically, 85 per cent of the species and subspecies of birds in the world occur only in tropical regions, leaving only 15 per cent in temperate or cold climes. Moreover, two-thirds of all the birds in the tropics live in humid climates rather than in the arid ones.

Geologically, we are assured that, especially in Miocene and Pliocene time, humid, tropical climates occupied a much greater part of the earth's surface than they do now, so that the arctic regions were very much less extensive than they are now.

For the sake of convenience and clarity a rough table is appended, showing the succession of geological ages and the appearance and development of birds.

ARCHAEAN OR EOZOIC

PALAEOZOIC OR PRIMARY — development of invertebrates
    Cambrian
    Silurian   — first true fishes
    Devonian
    Carboniferous
    Permian

MESOZOIC OR SECONDARY — Age of Reptiles
    Triassic
    Jurassic   — first bird, Archaeopteryx
    Cretaceous   — strange toothed birds, Hesperornis and Ichthyornis

CENOZOIC OR TERTIARY	—	Age of Mammals
Eocene	—	appearance of modern bird orders
Oligocene	—	" " " " "
Miocene	—	first passerine bird; modern bird families
Pliocene	—	development of modern genera and species
QUARTERNARY	—	Age of Man
Pleistocene	—	glacial epoch or Ice Age
Recent	—	post glacial time

In late Pliocene and in Pleistocene time a rapid refrigeration of climate took place, which culminated in the well-known Ice Age, and during the maximum period of refrigeration it is believed that the mean annual temperature in the northern hemisphere dropped by as much as 7 degrees Centigrade. Not only did this force the wholesale migration of animals and birds to the southward, but it also involved extinction on a colossal scale.

It was during Pliocene times in particular that many modern families of mammals and birds reached their present limits in the tropics, and a great many of them today survive only in the tropics and are unknown in cold and temperate climates.

Topographically, there have also been profound changes in the map of the world in the long spaces of geological time. As regards the New World, we need to know only two or three of these past changes. For a considerable period, before the Ice Age, Asia and North America were connected by land over what is now Bering Strait, and birds and mammals were able to pass from one hemisphere

to the other, thus accounting for the present-day homo-
geneity of the Holarctic Region. It is more than probable
that there was also land connection between North America and Europe, via Greenland, but at the moment we do
not care whether this proves to be true or not.

It is equally important to remember that South America
was separated from North America for long periods, up
to and through early Miocene time, and consequently no
mammals, nor the more sedentary birds which originated
in the northern hemisphere, could possibly have reached
South America until Miocene time at the earliest.

The fossil record proves to us that modern bird orders
and families originated in Eocene time, that the principal
development of these modern families took place in Miocene time, and that genera and species originated in
Pliocene and late Pliocene time, and it is possible, though by
no means proved, that some modern distinct species did not
originate until early Pleistocene time. Paleontologists seem
to agree that a million or more years are required to evolve
really distinct types. Subspecies and the more technical
"species" discussed in Chapter X are a different matter.

The fossil record also shows overwhelmingly that the
present-day distribution of birds and mammals can be
utterly different from what it was in the past. As an example, I cite the gorgeously colored trogons, a purely
tropical group of birds, noted for their brilliant shimmering
green backs and wings and their crimson or golden-yellow
under parts. Today, the great majority of trogons are found
in the New World tropics, in South and Central America.

TROPICAL RAIN FOREST
Sambu River, Darien

GUATEMALA PINE FOREST ABOVE LAKE ATITLAN

(See p. 141.)

There are comparatively few in the Oriental tropics, in India, the Malay peninsula, and the East Indies, and there are only three or four in tropical Africa. On the basis of present-day facts, who would have imagined that the trogons are a family that first appeared in the Eocene of France?

As a summary of these various facts, I wish to point out that the distribution of any modern group of birds or mammals is, consequently, the product of the following factors:

1. Where and when the group originated.

2. What land bridges were available by which this group could reach various other continents.

3. How far south this group was driven during the Ice Age, and to what degree it was exterminated by this remarkable climatic change.

4. To what extent, if any, it has migrated northward again with the recession of the Ice Sheets, and has consequently recaptured territory which was rendered available for colonization in the very recent past.

The continent of Australia furnishes an excellent example. Geologically, history proves that Australia has been separated from all other great land masses for the longest period of time, with the result that a very fair percentage of well-known bird families, otherwise world-wide in their distribution, are lacking, for the very simple reason that they did not originate until all land connections between the East Indies and Australia had ceased. Similarly, the great majority of the modern families of mammals are entirely lacking there. North America is regarded as the Nearctic subregion of the Holarctic region, due to various peculiar factors which will be the principal subject of a later chapter. Thanks to the fossil record, we may postulate that the bird and mammal life of North America was formerly infinitely richer and more varied than it is now. Many tropical groups either originated in North America or occurred here for greater or less periods of geological time, and we know that the continent swarmed with elephants, tapirs, rhinoceroses, horses, and tigers, to mention only a minute fraction of the great mammal fauna that it formerly possessed.

It is perhaps unfortunate that the concept of these zoological regions was based primarily on the mammals and birds—the two most recent groups of animals to evolve on earth. But they happen to be the best known, and the mammals have the very best fossil record of any animals. It follows from these remarks that our concept of zoogeographical regions does not apply so well to other groups of living things, such as the plants and most of the older groups of animals. The major plant families have a history immeasurably more ancient than those of mammals and birds, and they originated many, many millions of years before these two groups of animals appeared on earth. The result is that families and even genera of plants are not characteristic of one continent in particular. The principal families of plants are of world-wide distribution, and, in addition, many genera have a type of spotty distribution which is absolutely unknown in the most recent groups of small song and perching birds. The buttercups,[1] a most familiar group of flowers to all, are found not only throughout the north temperate region, but also reappear in the south temperate portions of the world. There are buttercups in New Zealand, and there are buttercups in South Africa, and there are buttercups in southern Australia. Quite a number of plants of the eastern United States are otherwise found only in China and Japan. Other groups of plants occur in the southern United States and Australia. No modern genus of birds has a distribution even remotely resembling this.

Because of the effects of a longer series of climatic changes, and questions of soil deposition and formation, the world is divided into numerous phytogeographic regions which are totally different from those of mammals and birds. A portion of Cape Colony in South Africa is a very distinct floral region, and there is not one single mammal or bird to lend support to the evidence supplied by the peculiarities of the flora.

REFERENCES

1. WALLACE, ALFRED RUSSEL. *The Geographical Distribution of Animals*. 2 vols. London, 1876.
       Now very much out of date in many respects, but still gives a clear picture in simple language of the great zoogeographic regions, and the better known animals characteristic of each.
2. LYDEKKER, RICHARD. Zoological Distribution. Article in *Encyclopedia Britannica*, 11th edition, vol. 28, 1911, pp. 1001–1018.
3. WATSON, D. C. SEARES. Zoological Regions. Article in *Encyclopedia Britannica*, 14th edition, vol. 23, 1936, pp. 964–973.

[1] As to the genus *Ranunculus* only, not the family.

4. HESSE, R. Distribution of Animals. Article in *Encyclopedia Britannica*, 14th edition, vol. 7, pp. 432–443.

Of particular interest, as it is written from the standpoint of the limiting effects of fundamental factors such as light, temperature, moisture, altitude, marine versus fresh-water or terrestrial life, etc.

5. WETMORE, ALEXANDER. Birds of the Past. Smithsonian *Report* for 1928, pp. 377–389.

CHAPTER VII

DISTRIBUTION: SOUTH AMERICA

RECALLING that 85 per cent of all birds are found in the tropics, the famous wealth of bird-life in tropical America should be examined first. Proceeding northward, and gradually leaving tropical climates behind, in temperate North America we reach areas only recently recaptured from the Pleistocene Ice Age, and the pure Arctic comes last of all.

Any division of a zoogeographic region into smaller areas is difficult and involves tedious questions of terminology. Here confusion reigns supreme, and people have talked about biotic provinces, divisions, districts, life zones, and faunal areas or faunas, very often using these terms in totally different senses. The criteria are also in dispute and vary widely from one group of animals to another, and different criteria produce disappointingly different results. I shall have more to say about this in a later chapter on North America. But there is now general agreement, at least among ornithologists, that a region is divided into Subregions, that tropical climates are divided into faunas, and that life zones are altitudinal and consequently require mountain ranges, and are based on decreasing temperature with increasing altitude. It is the presence of mountains rising from a tropical base that produces the most concentrated bird-life known on earth.

Faunas, in the zoogeographic sense, are relatively small areas where, because of humidity or other variations in climate, or isolation of one kind or another, there is a marked percentage of what are called *endemic* genera and species. An endemic genus or species of bird is a genus or species found in one particular fauna and nowhere else on earth.

The main features of South America are obvious in any atlas map. It extends south into temperate climates, and there is, consequently, a very distinct and definite temperate subregion with a peculiar fauna in southern South America. Among the birds there are numerous waterfowl, many tinamous, the rhea, the peculiar families of seed-snipe and plant-cutters, a great variety of oven-birds, flycatchers, and finches, to mention only a few.

Shortly after reaching tropical latitudes in northern Argentina and Paraguay, a great stretch of rolling tableland includes most of the southern half of Brazil, known as the Campo country, with a distinct fauna and flora. It is relatively open country, with a semi-arid climate, covered with a mixture of savannas and patches of scrub woodland, but the high, dense woodland tends to be strictly confined to the margins of the principal watercourses. It was through this Campo country that President Theodore Roosevelt made his famous expedition down the River of Doubt and finally reached Amazonian drainage.

The tablelands or the Campos of Brazil sink gradually northward into the gigantic river basin of the Amazon, probably the greatest river system on earth, with the greatest area of tropical rain forest on earth. It stretches from the mouth of the Amazon to the base of the Andes, 3,000 miles to the west, and extends north to the Caribbean coast of the Guianas. It includes the entire drainage basin of the almost equally gigantic Orinoco River, and the only major variation in this enormous area is that, particularly in the Orinoco basin, there are considerable areas of savanna or grassy plains instead of a dense forest such as is characteristic of the Amazon River basin proper. It possesses an enormous fauna and flora, and constitutes the Amazonian Subregion.

The outstanding geographic feature of the continent, however, is the chain of the mighty Andes, stretching its entire length, and reaching well above snow line in tropical latitudes. There is a relatively narrow Pacific coastal plain. A factor here of the greatest importance in geological history is that the lowlands came first in South America, and the Andes came later, being a very recent range of mountains which started to rise in Tertiary time. Consequently, when they reached altitudes in excess of 5,000 feet, all tropical birds on either side of those mountains were perpetually separated from or "isolated" from each other, with the result that on the Pacific coastal plain of South America there are some very sharp and definite "faunas," the nearest relatives of which are the Amazonian humid forest birds; but, due to this prolonged period of isolation, they have evolved into a large number of distinct species and some peculiar genera.

The second factor to be considered in understanding the

origin of these faunas is the question of humidity. The whole west coast of Colombia, which is the most northwestern republic in South America, has the most humid climate known in the New World, and 400 inches of rain have been recorded there in one year. This humid climate extends south down the Pacific coast to northern Ecuador, and is then replaced by a much more arid climate which continues on down the coast to northern Peru, where begins a stretch several hundred miles long of severe desert.

There are, consequently, three distinct bird faunas on the Pacific coast of tropical South America. There is the Peruvian Desert Fauna; the Equatorial Arid Fauna; and to the north, in the exceedingly humid climate of Colombia and Darien, there is a very distinct fauna, which Dr. F. M. Chapman named the Colombian-Pacific Fauna. It should be noted that in tropical latitudes at sea level there are ideal and uniform temperature conditions, and it is the humidity only which varies.

In mountain ranges, such as the Andes, not only humidity but temperature varies, and, as one ascends the Andes in Ecuador and Colombia, one passes through four climatic zones. We start with the tropics at their base. At 5,000 feet begins the subtropical zone, where cooler temperatures prevail, where the climate is always intensely humid, and where it rains throughout the year. At 8,000 feet the temperate zone is reached, where there is a cool, temperate climate. There may be both humid and arid sections, depending upon the presence or absence of what is called a "rain shadow." Tree line lies above the temperate zone in

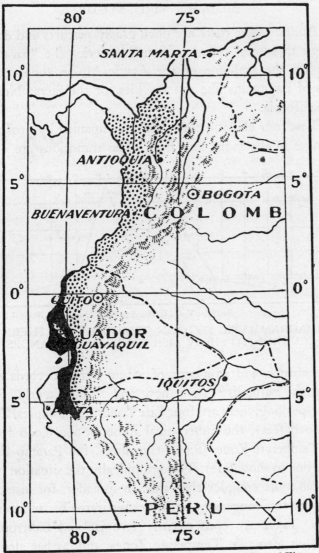

COLOMBIAN–PACIFIC AND EQUATORIAL
ARID FAUNAS OF SOUTH AMERICA

the Andes, where there are open grassy pastures and damp, boggy meadows, called in South America the "paramo," roughly the analogue of the Arctic-Alpine zone on the tops of mountains like the Rockies, or the Sierra Nevada in California.

These four climatic zones are accompanied by profound changes in the fauna and flora. The transitions are often

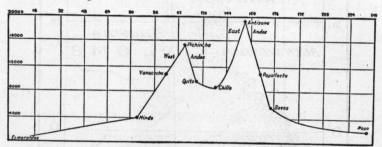

DIAGRAMMATIC SECTION THROUGH NORTHERN
ECUADOR TO SHOW LIFE ZONES OF THE ANDES

quite abrupt, and an ascent of a few hundred yards may bring the naturalist into a new and strange world. Faunally speaking, there are four Life Zones: the Tropical Zone (0–5,000 feet), the Subtropical Zone (5,000–8,000 feet), the Temperate Zone (8,000–tree line), the Paramo Zone (tree line to snow line). Topographically the situation may be even more complex than this. In Ecuador, for instance, there are *two* ranges of the Andes separated by an interior valley. There are consequently two isolated Subtropical Zones, at least two Temperate Zones, and, as has already been explained, the birds of the Tropical Zone in the

Pacific lowlands are very different from those at the eastern base of the Eastern Andes. In Colombia there are *three* principal ranges of the Andes.

The resultant wealth of bird-life concentrated in a relatively small total mileage is the greatest in the world. The total distance across Ecuador, as the crow flies, is about 240 miles, but if we took a year on the journey, and stopped in each Life Zone for a reasonable period of time, we would find a possible total of 1,780 species of birds.

Roughly speaking, the birds of the Subtropical and Temperate Zones are highly modified descendants of tropical ancestors, and naturally those of the Temperate Zone are often so very different that there are no obvious relatives living at tropical levels today. The birds of the Paramo Zone, interestingly enough, are species which occur at sea level in temperate South America. As these birds range northward, they find similar temperatures and habitat conditions at ever-increasing altitudes in the high Andes. This situation is analogous to one prevailing in the eastern United States. Many birds nesting at sea level in northern Maine breed also on the summit of Mount Greylock, Massachusetts (2,500–3,500 feet), and in the mountains of North Carolina at 4,000–6,500 feet.

Exactly the same principles of zonal distribution apply to other mountain masses in South America, such as are found in Venezuela, the hinterland of British Guiana, and eastern Brazil. All are isolated, arise from tropical bases and have peculiar birds in their Subtropical and Temperate Zones.

It is consequently a popular misconception to think of
South America or the Neotropical Region as tropical. A
substantial portion of the continent extends south of the
Tropic of Capricorn, and has an exceedingly cold, windy,
and disagreeable climate. In numerous mountain ranges
there are extensive areas also, in which, because of altitude,
tropical temperatures do not prevail, and to which many
characteristic Neotropical mammals and birds are confined.
Less than half the known birds of South America occur in
the "tropics," as popularly thought of. When the un-
traveled American thinks of the tropics he pictures a dense,
evergreen jungle inhabited by noxious insects, poisonous
snakes, birds of incredibly brilliant and gaudy plumage,
jaguars, ocelots, and tapirs. He forgets the effects of altitude, the existence of deserts, and is astonished to learn
that there are extensive areas with a relatively arid climate,
in which the country dries up and the trees lose their
leaves for a portion of each year.

He is really thinking of the humid tropics, which require an annual rainfall of 80 to 120 inches, more or less
dispersed *throughout the year*, to produce the dense rain
forest of which he has read. Such conditions are unknown
in temperate latitudes, and certain characteristics of the
bird-life of the humid tropics are worth describing.

In the first place the majority of the birds there are non-
migratory. The breeding season is irregular and takes place
throughout the year. Not only is this true of one kind of
bird, as compared with another, but it is equally true of
different individuals of the same bird. Thus, a proportion

of individuals of the quail in Panama nest in April at the beginning of the rainy season, and a certain percentage nest in October at the end of the rainy season. Perhaps this double breeding season tends to reduce the competition, as far as this particular species is concerned.

One of the important and fundamental characteristics of the tropics is an abundant and an easily procured food supply, which can be counted upon throughout the year. Compared with temperate regions, there is a great abundance and variety of species, but a corresponding scarcity of individuals. The rarity of a great many birds in the tropics is so remarkable and so extraordinary that it is almost impossible to see how the species manages to survive. While in common parlance in bird study here in the States we talk of a given bird as rare, there is no such thing as a really rare bird in the northern hemisphere, with the few exceptions of birds which are on the verge of extinction because of persecution by man. There are several birds found in Costa Rica, of which only three to six specimens have been secured in three-quarters of a century, with every naturalist and collector eagerly on the lookout during that whole period.

There is also an astounding refinement of habitat, which has no parallel in north temperate regions. The rain forest is divided into at least six fundamentally distinct zones. There is the forest floor. There are the bushes and the tangled thickets that grow on the forest floor. There are special palm jungles of a peculiar species in Central America, and it is only in the jungles of this particular palm that a certain flycatcher (*Aphanotriccus capitalis*) occurs. By wandering around, looking for a second jungle of this particular species of palm, you can be reasonably sure of finding one more pair.

Coming back to the forest and its divisions, the trunks of the trees, to the first main branches, are occupied by a whole fauna of birds, so to speak; the branches from sixty to 100 feet constitute the home of another large group of species; and, finally, there is the crown, where sunlight is readily available, though entirely out of sight and gunshot from the ground, occupied by another great group of birds and a whole special fauna of insects. A recent expedition to British Guiana successfully worked this fauna by building platforms and ladders in the tops of the trees, and observers were stationed in these platforms throughout the daylight hours. In three weeks they got many new species of insects.

In my own work in eastern Panama, the only way that I secured a sample of this particular bird fauna was by finding some gigantic trees which were growing next to a knife-like ridge, and by ascending to the top of the ridge I was in gunshot range of the top of one of the trees. After clearing the underbrush from the base of the tree in a circle about fifty yards square, I stood on the ridge and shot into the top of the tree, and my friends stood in the cleared space at the bottom and gathered up such birds as fell. In this way we added several South American birds to Panama, and discovered several new to science in the course of two mornings.

A certain thick-billed seed-eater (*Oryzoborus nuttingi*) dwells in beds of gigantic rushes averaging about ten feet high and three or four feet deep. There are several rivers with this rush in eastern Nicaragua, and this particular seed-eater is confined to the reed-beds of those rivers, and is found nowhere else.

In the great river basin of the Amazon there are a large number of birds that will not cross a wide river, and their range is, consequently, bounded by the area of land between any two of the main tributaries.

As an example of the wealth of bird-life in the humid tropics, there are 1,100 species of birds on the lower third of the Amazon. In eastern Costa Rica four hundred species of birds have been found in a walking radius of five miles from a certain hamlet. In Panama I have listed far more species of birds than there are in the whole continent of North America, in spite of the fact that the area of the Republic of Panama is approximately that of New York State.

By way of contrast, consider the State of Massachusetts. Here there is a cool temperate climate, and in addition it is an arid climate in the sense that the annual rainfall is way below the optimum of 100 inches per year. The temperature is not uniform, and conditions are unendurable for most birds for most of the year. As a consequence, they are highly migratory, and there are very few permanent residents. The breeding season is limited to a brief period of the year, when optimum conditions prevail, and competition for the meager food supply is greatly increased. Such a refinement of habitat as I have just mentioned for the tropics is impossible in any north temperate region, owing to the absolute necessity of the birds ranging over a much wider area for food. We have a corresponding scarcity of variety of species, and a greatly increased abundance of individuals of most of them. Imagine the fate of birds in Massachusetts that couldn't or wouldn't cross a river! It follows that they would have become extinct long before our time.

The rigors of environment and the lack of sharp, climatic contrasts naturally tend to discourage the development of faunas in temperate climates. The factors of isolation so common in the tropics are absent. Mountain ranges have a greatly reduced effect, since the lowlands on each side of the range, and the whole range itself, are all in the Temperate Zone to start with. The Alleghenies, one of the oldest mountain chains on earth, have produced only six to ten peculiar *subspecies* of birds.

REFERENCES

1. CHAPMAN, F. M. Distribution of Bird-Life in Colombia. *Bulletin of the American Museum of Natural History*, vol. 36, 1917. Introduction, pp. 70–169.
2. CHAPMAN, F. M. Distribution of Bird-Life in Ecuador. *Bulletin of the American Museum of Natural History*, vol. 55, 1926. Introduction, pp. 23–133.

CHAPTER VIII

DISTRIBUTION: CENTRAL AMERICA

PROCEEDING northward into Central America, distributional problems of considerable interest arise, owing to certain new conditions. (1) Central America is an exceedingly small and narrow strip of land with a series of central mountain masses. Historically, diametrically opposite conditions to those pertaining in the Andes prevail. The mountain masses are of great geological antiquity, and the present-day tropical lowlands of the coastal strips are of Quaternary or recent geological time. It follows that the birds now found there can only have come from three possible sources: (a) the north; (b) the south; or (c) the adjacent interior mountains.

(2) Another historical factor of great effect was the refrigeration of climate during the Ice Age. The present-day tropical lowlands of Mexico, and northern Central America at least, could not possibly have had such a climate during this period, and many tropical birds must have been driven far south of their present limits. Considerable northward immigration must have taken place since.

(3) The mountain masses in Central America are discontinuous, again in contrast to the Andes. There is the well-known "break" at the Isthmus of Panama. Another

break, in the lowlands of southern Nicaragua, was once picked as the site of a possible canal, but the idea was abandoned because of the near proximity of active volcanoes. There is a third in the Isthmus of Tehuantepec in southern Mexico.

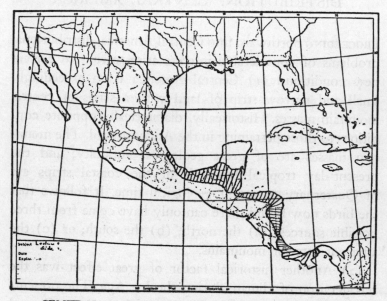

CENTRAL AMERICAN HUMID TROPICAL FAUNA

(4) In northern Central America, especially in the mountains, the transition from tropical to temperate faunas takes place, and in Mexico the Temperate Zone reaches sea level.

Let us consider the tropical lowlands first. The area on the Caribbean slope of Central America, north to Vera

Cruz, Mexico, contains the Central American Humid Tropical Fauna. It is quite distinct from the one in western Colombia and eastern Panama, even though the forest is continuous. Perhaps the chief reason is the greatly decreased rainfall, which almost never exceeds 150 inches a year. But those who have lived in a tent in this forest in the rainy season, as I have, would not think of it as a dry climate.

A great many birds are common to these two faunas, not only occupying the entire Colombian-Pacific Fauna, but also ranging north into eastern Central America. Statistically, the birds break up approximately as follows:

Fauna	Endemic genera	Endemic species
Colombian-Pacific	5	186
Central American Humid	5	35
Common to both	16	57

The remaining elements of this Central American Fauna are South American birds which occur east of the Andes. With so few endemics, it is really depauperate in character, and most of the birds have probably come in recently from the south. Group after group of the characteristic South American or Neotropical birds decreases northward in Central America. In addition, the total number of species rapidly decreases northward, and finally, in the case of any one particular species, a bird which is common in southern Central America is uncommon in middle Central

America and exceedingly rare or unknown in northern Central America. There are four hundred species of birds, for instance, in the tropical lowlands of eastern Costa Rica. There are only two hundred species of birds in eastern

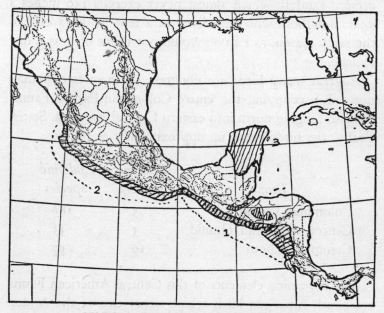

CENTRAL AMERICAN ARID FAUNA

Guatemala, and there are only one hundred and fifty in eastern Mexico. In all this area, the amount of rainfall is the same, and the mean annual temperature has fallen only three degrees between the Canal Zone and eastern Mexico.

On the opposite or Pacific side of Central America, in the rain shadow of the central backbone of the mountains, there is a relatively arid climate, in which the rainfall varies from only 40 to 80 inches a year with a prolonged dry season, and this climate extends up the coast to the limit of tropical climates in western Mexico. It is inhabited by a very distinct fauna which has much less variety of species than is found in the humid tropics on the opposite side of the continent, but contains no less than 11 peculiar genera and 41 peculiar species. Here and there, in interior valleys, there are some arid or semi-desert pockets which are also occupied by birds which are members of this fauna, and the outer tip of the Yucatan peninsula is also relatively arid, with much the same group of birds, in spite of the intervening belt of humid tropics.

The great distinctness of the Pacific Arid Fauna is due to two principal factors; the tropical birds that have come in from the south are highly modified by adaptation to an arid instead of a humid climate, and a second group of birds has obviously descended to the tropical coastal plains from the adjacent mountains. This is proved by the fact that their relatives all range north of but not south of this particular fauna.

The outstanding features of the Subtropical Zone in the central mountains (3,000–6,000 feet) are the humidity of the climate and the density of vegetation, though the height of the trees is reduced. It rains or at least drizzles every day of the year, and, except in the early morning, clouds hang low over the mountains most of the day. It only pours every now and then, perhaps, for an hour once every 24 or 48 hours. In 1924 we lived for two weeks in the mountains of Veraguas, western Panama, and my party is the only one as yet fortunate enough to have reached this country and stayed there a reasonable length of time. One day we had a real downpour, 9½ inches of rain in 55 minutes! On a world-wide basis, this is really a humid climate!

The Temperate Zone, as already mentioned, may be either humid or arid, depending upon whether higher mountains cut off the moisture-laden winds. In Central America the high mountains of western Panama and Costa Rica possess only a humid Temperate Zone from 6,000 to 11,000 feet. The climate is very cool, and a light overcoat or a sweater is needed at night. The humidity features are about the same as in the lower altitudes of the Subtropical Zone, but heavy downpours are, as far as I know, unknown. The density of the vegetation and the resultant conditions almost defy description. The trees are loaded with parasites and moss; the ground is so deeply buried in moss that one never sees any solid earth. A man sinks a foot or two in wet moss at every step, and it is impossible to keep dry. The footing is really dangerous; the tree-roots are all interlaced, the chinks usually concealed with moss, and one can get a bad tumble. The hardest thing I had to learn at 7,500 feet in western Panama was to shoot birds only directly over my head; those shot at an angle could never be seen to hit the ground; they plunked into the soft moss and disappeared, and usually it was *absolutely impossible* to get to the spot where they fell in a beeline, with the natural result that the exact spot was lost. It was a great thrill for an exploring naturalist to spend two days and a night alone on the Continental Divide, to see both the Atlantic and Pacific Oceans at dawn, and to collect nine birds new to science. But it was aggravating to have to wait until some of them chose to come directly overhead.

In Guatemala the humid Temperate Zone exists only in patches at high altitudes (8,000–10,000 feet or more). As in the Andes, there are many remarkable and peculiar birds in the Temperate Zone in Costa Rica, and a different lot in Guatemala. All are little known, with nothing but Latin names, and there is no point in listing them here. One bird in Guatemala, however, would astound the northern bird student interested in warblers. It is obviously a warbler, but bright pink all over, and the unprepared visitor would certainly think there was something the matter with him.

Recalling what I said on an earlier page about the "breaks" in the mountains in Central America, I wish to emphasize the essential discontinuity of the Subtropical and Temperate Zones in the mountains of Central America. Even in the gigantic Andes the Temperate Zone is divided into numerous isolated areas. These should consequently be thought of as islands in a sea of lower altitudes, and it should be remembered that their birds are as strictly resident and confined to these zonal islands as are landbirds on a real island in the ocean. Small wonder then that this isolation has resulted in many endemic genera, species, and subspecies.

But perhaps of even greater biological interest are those

cases where, in spite of inevitable discontinuity of distribution, the same species of bird occurs over a very extensive area. This is an outstanding characteristic of the birds in the Subtropical Zone in Central America, which is merely a feeble continuation northward of a much richer

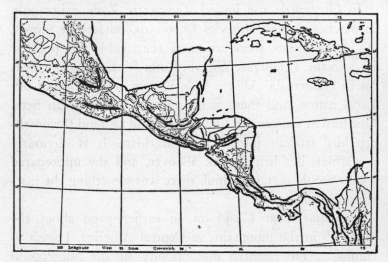

CENTRAL AMERICAN SUBTROPICAL ZONE ISLANDS

fauna in the Andes. Nevertheless, the majority of the species range continuously from Colombia to southern Mexico. This is a really difficult thing for the naturalist to explain. I have elsewhere suggested that, at the period of maximum refrigeration of the Ice Age, the Subtropical Zone fauna was forced down to sea level, and that the birds consequently had a continuous range. With the return of warmer climates they ascended the mountains to favorable altitudes, thus acquiring their present discontinuous distribution.

An even more remarkable case of discontinuous distribution is exemplified by the short-billed marsh wren, which ranges widely over the eastern United States in temperate climates at sea level, and ranges south on isolated high mountain savannas in the Andes to Peru and Bolivia. Large areas of the Temperate Zone are, of course, entirely unsuitable, as they are covered with heavy forest. It seems useless to speculate as to how this tiny bird ever acquired so remarkable a distribution.

Mention of the Arid Temperate Zone of Guatemala has been deliberately postponed to the last, as the transition to the bird-life of temperate North America takes place here, and the Neotropical Region has been left behind. Roughly speaking, the whole of the Altos of Guatemala above 5,000 feet are in this Zone, with the exception of the humid islands. The vegetation is a pine and oak forest, suggesting that of the mountains of southern Arizona. While the northern visitor will see some strange and unfamiliar birds, here for the first time he will find many familiar North American friends. There are ravens and crossbills; the brown creeper hitches up the tree trunks; flickers, chipping sparrows, and bluebirds are common; there is even a junco. This pine forest with most of the birds mentioned occurs south to the mountains of northern Nicaragua. All these boreal birds are recent immigrants from the north, driven south by the Ice Age, and are now marooned in these southern mountains, where they have found proper habitats and climatic conditions. It is more than likely that the pines and oaks moved south during the same period.

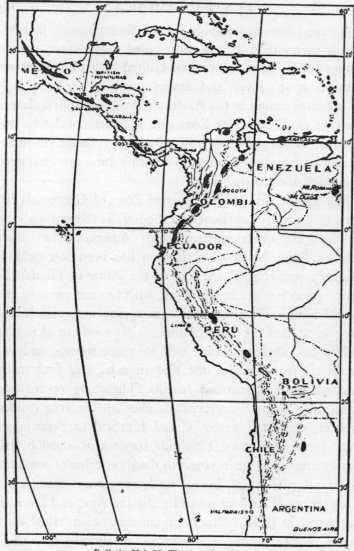

INTERRUPTED DISTRIBUTION OF THE SHORT–BILLED
MARSH WREN IN THE ANDEAN TEMPERATE ZONE

For many decades there has been debate among naturalists about a possible Central American subregion, but no
line or satisfactory boundaries have ever been drawn. To
sum up this chapter, there is no such subregion. The humid
tropics in Central America have a depauperate avifauna,
largely South American, with very few endemics. The arid
tropics possess far more peculiar species, but many of

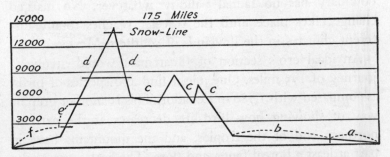

DIAGRAMMATIC SECTION THROUGH GUATEMALA
a = humid tropical; b = desert tropical; c = arid temperate; d = humid
temperate; e = subtropical; f = arid tropical

them are of northern origin. The Subtropical Zone birds
are identical with the South American. Only in the Humid
Temperate Zone in Guatemala and Costa Rica do we get
a highly distinct assemblage of peculiar types. The Arid
Temperate Zone birds are largely North American. The
real facts would appear to be that the Neotropical Region
extends north through Central America in two narrow
tongues, to the northern limits of rain forest at Tampico,
Mexico, and to the northern limits of the arid tropics on
the Pacific coast of Mexico in Sinaloa. The whole tableland of Mexico and much of the Altos of Guatemala are

faunally part of North America, and consequently belong to the Nearctic Region.

It must be emphasized that biological and political boundaries rarely coincide. In spite of the reasons of convenience that led the American Ornithologists' Union to adopt the United States—Mexico boundary as the southern limit of the Check-List of North American birds, this boundary has no faunal validity whatever. No marked change takes place until the traveler reaches totally different climates in the lowlands of southern Mexico.

An ideal cross section of Guatemala would involve a journey of 175 miles. One might find 450 species of birds, as compared with 1,780 in Ecuador. This is another graphic way of showing how bird-life decreases at the extreme northern end of the tropics, and the mountains have in part at least a boreal fauna and flora. The real cause of the decrease is the loss of optimum variety in the way of climate, and a reduction in the number of factors of isolation. Ecuador possesses every possible advantage in these respects, and consequently can claim one bird out of every thirteen on earth. Needless to say, the area of Ecuador is only a minute decimal of one per cent of the total land mass of the planet. In North America there are only three climates in strict comparison, arctic, arid, and mildly humid temperate. Even lofty mountain ranges cannot produce factors of isolation of comparable biological importance. A recent Ice Age and present-day rigorous and uniform conditions account for the mere 600-odd species in the entire continent.

REFERENCES

1. GRISCOM, LUDLOW. Ornithology of the Republic of Panama. *Bulletin of the Museum of Comparative Zoology*, vol. 78, no. 3, April, 1935, pp. 269–289.
2. GRISCOM, LUDLOW. Distribution of Bird-Life in Guatemala. *Bulletin of the American Museum of Natural History*, vol. 64, May, 1932, pp. 15–77.
3. GRISCOM, LUDLOW. Origin and Relationships of the Faunal Areas of Central America. *Proceedings of the Eighth American Scientific Congress*, vol. 3, May, 1940, pp. 425–430.

CHAPTER IX

DISTRIBUTION: NORTH AMERICA

As REGARDS the science of zoogeography, North America, as defined in the preceding chapter, is termed the Nearctic Region or Subregion. According to one view, there are three Regions, an Arctic Region which goes around the world with a very limited but highly specialized fauna; the Palaearctic Region (Europe, North Africa, and northern Asia); and North America or the Nearctic Region. Another view calls all this great land mass the Holarctic Region, the three elements being reduced to Subregions. There are excellent arguments for both positions, but the matter is far too technical for discussion here; as usual it is largely a choice between emphasizing resemblances or differences. It is certain that in the millions of years that the orders and families of mammals and birds have been evolving and migrating from continent to continent, as opportunity offered or climatic change compelled, they wasted no effort in trying to remain within the man-made boundaries of these various Regions. It would be much less interesting if they had!

An analysis of the distribution of the families of birds may serve to bring out some points of interest in two different directions. Those families which are "peculiar" to the New World, which occur only in the New World and not in the Old World, will be considered first. I could, of course, in a thorough scientific survey, take up the genera and the species also, but this would involve us in far too many technicalities. There are forty-four families of birds that are found only in the New World. Of these, thirty-two families occur only in tropical America, and only sixteen of these barely reach tropical southern Mexico, where they are represented by one, two, or three species only. The remaining twelve families range north into the United States. But the overwhelming majority of the species concerned are highly migratory and return to the tropics for the winter. It is of interest to note, in passing, that these birds greatly predominate in the more humid eastern United States, as compared to the more arid western United States. These facts give a good endorsement for establishing the northern limits of the Neotropical Region, and they further prove the depauperate nature of Central American bird-life and its South American origin.

This is an illustration of the principle of recapture of territory since the retreat of the Ice Age. When New England was buried under 1,000 feet of ice, when the arctic musk ox ranged as far south as Tennessee, and the subarctic great auk went to Florida in the winter, where were the insect-eating flycatchers, the vireos, the warblers, the tanagers ninety per cent of whose relatives are now and always have been in the tropics? Needless to say, their northern limits must have been 800 to 1,000 miles farther south than they are at the present moment, and they could not possibly have endured the conditions of New England or anything remotely resembling them during the maximum extent of the ice.

An interesting paper reached me recently, announcing the discovery of an early Pleistocene spruce bog in central Texas. An analysis of the pollen grains and spores in peat deposits proved that spruce, hemlock, and balsam grew in central Texas approximately one hundred thousand years ago, and the locality is 800 miles farther south than the present southernmost limit of spruce in the North American continent.

To proceed with our analysis of the families of birds in the New World, it follows that all of the remaining families, besides the forty-four tropical ones just mentioned, are also found in the Old World. There are fifty-eight of them. Over one-half of these are cosmopolitan groups of water-birds, seafowl, and birds of prey which, geologically, are of particularly ancient origin, whose presence in the New World could have been expected as a matter of absolute certainty, and has no special significance.

The remaining families are, however, easily divisible into four great groups. In the first place, there are the loons and the alcids, the alcids containing such familiar northern sea-birds as guillemots, puffins, and auks. These two families are endemic in the boreal parts of the northern hemisphere, nesting in arctic and subarctic climates and wintering various degrees farther southward. Consequently, two peculiar families in part serve to characterize the Holarctic Region.

Secondly, there are eight families whose representatives

J. P. Chapin

CORY'S SHEARWATER

Off Monomoy Point, Massachusetts

SNOWY OWL

in the New World are genera and species closely related
to or identical with Old World types. The horned lark,
brown creeper, and arctic nesting pipit are all species common to both hemispheres. The northern shrike is merely
a subspecies of the great gray shrike of Europe. There are
only three species of waxwings, all Holarctic, and one of
them, the Bohemian, goes around the world. With the
dippers and nuthatches the genus is identical, but the North
American species are distinct. The wren-tit of California
is barely separable generically from certain Chinese members of the vast Old World family of babblers (Timaliidae).

Another important point is that the larks and shrikes
are very large Old World families with numerous genera
and species. There are only one lark and two shrikes in
the New World; while a much smaller total number, all
creepers are Old World birds. The babblers have already
been mentioned. This is a clear indication of the probable
Old World origin of these families, and their relatively recent immigration to the New. The fact that two of these
families (the wren-tit and the dipper) occur only in the
far west, in other words in those sections of the continent
closest to the old Bering Strait land bridge, corroborates
this view.

Thirdly, there is another group of families which have
apparently invaded the New World on two or more occasions, and the question arises as to how we infer this. It can
be seen that some of the genera and species in these families
are identical with genera or species which go around the
world. But, in addition to these closely related or identical

genera and species, there are others which have been in the New World a much longer time, during which they have become highly differentiated. They are totally different from any relatives to be found in the Old World, and, indeed, we often cannot say that they represent any particular member of the family in the Old World.

For example, in the grouse, or game birds, there are two species of arctic ptarmigan both of which go around the entire world. Our ruffed grouse represents the hazel-hen of Europe. They can be contrasted with curious American types like the sage grouse and the prairie chicken, or heath hen; there is no game bird remotely resembling either type in the Old World.

In the woodpecker family, the three-toed woodpeckers range throughout the boreal parts of the Northern Hemisphere. Compare them with a totally distinct and peculiar group of woodpeckers, like the flickers, which are so familiar in the United States. There are many special woodpeckers in the New World, including a number of tropical genera. In between these two extremes, so to speak, is the genus Dryobates, common to both hemispheres, with numerous North American species, all quite distinct from those in Europe and Asia. Among them are our familiar hairy and downy woodpeckers, and it is both interesting and significant to find in Europe a similar pair of species, almost identical in coloration, but markedly different in size. It is extremely doubtful if such striking correspondences are the product of chance; it is quite possible that all four are descended from a common ancestor.

In the swallow family, the barn swallow and the bank swallow go around the world without any substantial variation. Contrast them with the purple martin and other species of martins in tropical America, which are quite different from other swallows found elsewhere.

With the titmice, there are the familiar chickadees some of which, at least, are specifically identical with European species or others in eastern Asia. They may be contrasted with the little birds of the southwestern deserts, such as the verdin, or the bushtits, which belong in a special subfamily.

In the crow family, the raven goes around the entire world, and the magpie is at least in the western part of the United States, though it has not yet reached the east. A large variety of American jays are unlike any of the jays in the Old World.

Our two familiar kinglets illustrate the same principle. The golden-crowned closely represents a European species, but the ruby-crowned is very different. The New World gnatcatchers are the only other members of the great Old World family of warblers. They are so peculiar that their assignation to this family is by no means certain, but there is no family into which they obviously fit.

The largest family of birds in the world is the Fringillidae (finches, buntings, and sparrows, etc.). It is currently divided into three subfamilies, one of which is wholly New World and largely tropical. The Emberizinae or buntings contain our innumerable sparrows, towhees, and other closely related forms, and are better represented in this country than in the Old World. The remaining sub-family is primarily an Old World group. The pine grosbeak and the two crossbills go around the world; the rosy finches of our western mountains are also in eastern Asia; other genera are Holarctic, with distinct species in the two hemispheres.

Of these seven families, the grouse, titmice, crows, and true warblers are most abundant in the Old World, and possibly originated there. In most of them there are far more genera and species in western North America, sug-gesting that they reached the eastern states last. This state of affairs is reversed in the finch subfamily of buntings and sparrows. There are just as many genera and species peculiar to eastern North America as western. This fact, taken in connection with the greater development of the subfamily in North America as compared with the Old World, has given rise to the hypothesis that this subfamily originated in the New World. There is, however, no definite proof possible.

Fourth, and last, there is a group of families which in-vaded the New World so long ago and have undergone so much differentiation that it is difficult to say just what are their close relatives, if any, in the Old World. These families are now largely of tropical distribution in the New World.

The parrots are an outstanding illustration. There was only one member of the family in North America, the Carolina parakeet, which is now extinct. But there are many species of macaws, parrots, and parakeets in South

America, all very different from the innumerable parrots in Australia, tropical Asia, and Africa.

The cuckoos are also largely tropical in distribution. The trogons are entirely tropical. The swifts are largely tropical. There is a whole subfamily of American quail the majority of which are found south of the United States, and in a large family like the finches there is one whole subfamily which is characteristic of the tropics of the New World (Richmondeninae). There are only six kingfishers in the New World, and only one is North American. The number of migratory species wintering in the tropics in these families is notable, and as usual they predominate in the eastern states.

Passing now to an entirely different aspect of geographical distribution, North America can be divided into several grand divisions variously called realms or provinces. There is an arctic realm which, as we have already seen, possesses two peculiar families, the loons and the alcids, and there are also sixty endemic genera of birds in the arctic that go around the world. In addition, there are five characteristic American genera; examples are the snow geese and certain peculiar shore-birds, such as the buff-breasted and stilt sandpipers, the dowitcher, and the surf bird.

Below the arctic realm, from the northern limit of tree line south to the southern limit of the Canadian conifer forests or "north woods," there is a boreal province which also goes around the entire world, inhabited by two groups of birds; one, including the brown creeper, the two crossbills, and the pine grosbeak which are common to both hemispheres, and a few special American genera and a large number of purely American species, some of which clearly represent other species of the same genus in northern Europe and Asia. Examples are the ring-billed and Bonaparte's gulls, yellow rail, Clarke's nutcracker, the purple finches, pine siskin, winter wren, red-breasted nuthatch, Hudsonian chickadee, and golden-crowned kinglet, all belonging to genera with other species in the boreal parts of the Old World. These may be contrasted with a second group of such purely American types as the arctic three-toed woodpecker, varied thrush, gray-cheeked thrush, ruby-crowned kinglet, junco, and white-throated sparrow.

The balance of the continent is a debating ground between the Boreal Province and the great Mexican-Sonoran Subregion, which includes the whole tableland of Mexico, north to the deserts and more arid parts of the southwestern United States. It extends as far north as the interior drier portions of Washington and Oregon and Idaho. It includes the arid portions of southwestern Colorado, and extends east to central and southern Texas, including the Edwards Plateau of central Texas, and the coastal prairies, north at least as far as Rockport. This is one of the great centers of development of bird-life in the New World. There are no less than two peculiar families in this area, seventy-seven genera, and three hundred and four species. In addition to the special families, there are a great many other families in which whole groups of genera and species have been developed in this Subregion. For example, there is a great variety of jays, wrens, woodpeckers of certain genera, American quail, and orioles, and instances of this sort could be multiplied.

Certain species, members of the Mexican-Sonoran Subregion, have invaded the United States, and, pushing northward in relatively recent geological time, have become migratory, returning in the winter to their ancestral homes.

The balance of the continent contains the eastern United States, the Great Plains, and the Rocky Mountain states at higher altitudes. The bird-fauna is a hodgepodge of several elements, but there are two dominant ones: (a) birds belonging to highly modified Old World or cosmopolitan groups which predominate in the west, and (b) highly migratory birds of primarily Neotropical families, such as the numerous warblers, vireos, flycatchers, orioles, etc., which predominate in the east. These families have produced certain aggressive and dominant species that have pushed northward into the United States to breed, and they, too, return to their ancestral home the moment the breeding season is concluded.

One illustration of this is particularly graphic. There is a small, common, and well-known warbler in the eastern United States called the prairie warbler, which, among other things, has the peculiar nervous habit of constantly wagging its tail. It is abundant in the pine barrens and the sandy oak scrub of Cape Cod and Plymouth; it predominates in similar country on Long Island and in the New Jersey pine barrens, and it occurs locally in sandy areas inland. It migrates south to the West Indies in winter. The prairie warbler has only one very close relative in the great family of warblers, the vitelline warbler, which is tropical in distribution, and at the present time is found only on certain small islands in the West Indies, called the Cayman Islands, south of Cuba, and on Swan Island, one of the loneliest and most remote of oceanic islands right in the middle of the Caribbean Sea.

It is a remarkable and significant thing that the prairie warbler, in migrating southward to its present ancestral home in the West Indies, flies across the great expanse of water every fall from Cuba to the Cayman Islands, where it winters in abundance, while some individuals turn west and south and fly across the open Caribbean Sea to little Swan Island in the middle of the ocean, only seven square miles in area. It is on this ground that we infer that the prairie warbler and the vitelline warbler are probably descended from a common ancestor, that the latter has stayed in its tropical home, that it has not done well, surviving only on certain small islands, whereas the aggressive prairie warbler pushed northward into new country available for occupation in the States, and has thrived and multiplied.

The reader is entitled at this point to ask a searching question as to the justification for such speculations as these. There being no fossil record for these small songbirds whatever, how do we know that we are correct in speaking of these birds as Neotropical, and in assuming that the migratory species in the United States have pushed northward in recent geologic time? Why might it not be that they originated in North America, and that they have been pushing south into tropical America since long before the Ice Age? On the basis of what we know of trogons, and certain mammals, might they not have originated in some part of the Old World and become extinct there?

It is a good question. We know nothing about where these families of birds originated, but their *ancient* geological history does not concern us. When we speak of them as primarily Neotropical, we mean their *present-day* distribution, not that they originated in tropical America. Our speculations pertain only to their *recent* history. The Ice Age *must* have driven them 1,000 miles south of their present limits. All that we know of the antiquity of genera and species of birds makes it impossible for the biologist to argue that so many distinct genera and species originated in their present breeding ranges in postglacial time.

North America has three grand climatic and ecological divisions, south of the Boreal Subregion. There is a great forested and relatively humid area in the eastern states with twenty-five or more inches of rain a year. There are the plains and prairies of the central part of the country, and then there is a relatively arid western mountain area, in which the rainfall is from twenty-five inches all the way to zero. It is of great significance that the Mexican-Sonoran birds predominate in the arid western parts of the country, and that the more purely Neotropical families of birds, which have given the eastern United States their flycatchers, warblers, and tanagers, greatly predominate in the more humid sections of the eastern United States, just as their relatives predominate in the humid sections of the American tropics.

A few figures in this connection will, I trust, prove helpful. The Sonoran element is represented by 39 genera in the western United States, and 80 species. Only 17 of these genera reach the eastern United States, of which none is endemic, and only 17 species, one for each genus, reach the eastern United States, of which only 9 are peculiar.

If we turn to the purely Neotropical element, we find 53 genera and 91 species in the east; of these 10 genera and 67 of the 91 species are endemic. There are 43 of these genera in the west, with none endemic, and only 60 species, of which only 27 are endemic.

In all current books on the birds of the United States the country is divided into what are called Life-Zones, on the theory that eastern and western birds in the same latitudinal belt are more similar than northern and more southern birds. These are latitudinal bands which run across the country from east to west and are alleged to follow what are called isothermal lines. They consequently ignore the great division of the central plains, the break in the climate between the arid west and the relatively more humid east, and they also completely ignore the different origins of the two important elements of the avifauna. They are, consequently, biologically and ecologically unsound, and it is the greatest pity that Merriam's concept of these transcontinental Life-Zones happened to "take," so to speak, in the popular mind, instead of the much sounder divisions of J. A. Allen, which were made some years prior to Merriam's.

Merriam formulated two laws of temperature control

which I reproduce here. He claimed that animals and plants were restricted in their northward ranges by the total quantity of heat in the season of growth and reproduction. He also claimed that animals and plants were restricted southward by the mean temperature of the six hottest weeks. Curiously enough, the temperature calculations proved to have been made on an erroneous basis, and no corrections were ever made.

It is common sense, of course, that isothermal lines can be constructed, based on data supplied by the Weather Bureau; they can be run across the continent for every single degree of average temperature, either hotter or cooler; but, the fact remains that most birds pay little attention to them! We are unable to say that the northward distribution of any bird in the United States corresponds with any isothermal line; nor can we discover that its southern limits in the United States coincide with any isothermal line, based on the six hottest weeks. The botanists and the zoologists interested in other groups of animals besides birds have also carefully checked and rechecked this matter now for several decades, and few people believe any longer in these laws of temperature control.

The northward and southward limits of birds in North America are, actually, highly complex and elaborate combinations of factors, such as past history, the accident of survival, humidity, and the presence or absence of favorable habitat requirements.

In a great many cases territory in the northern states is still being recaptured by bird after bird of North America.

In my lifetime various birds have been steadily pushing northward and northeastward, and it follows, consequently, that the present isothermal lines of their northernmost limits are very much cooler than the isothermal lines that constituted their northern limits twenty-five years ago. In other words, it is obvious that temperature has not limited the northward distribution of these birds in any way whatsoever.

On the other hand, one or two examples can be given where temperature factors do limit the northward or the southward distribution of North American birds, where it has been positively proved by careful and continued observation. The white pelican winters in numbers on the Gulf Coast of Texas and practically every summer a certain number of white pelicans used to linger on their southern wintering grounds. They attempted to breed; they laid eggs, and the eggs hatched. But the young fried to death in the blazing heat of the Texas beaches in the May and June sun. It was some years before any white pelican succeeded in raising a young bird to maturity in the southern Texas area, and it seems reasonably clear that the extreme heat of the summer climate there is a limiting factor of great importance.

The Carolina wren of the eastern United States is a bird which is constantly pushing northward from Washington, D. C., as far as Massachusetts. At the end of a ten- or fifteen-year period, the bird is a general summer resident or rather a permanent resident throughout this area, with scattered pairs nesting in Massachusetts. All of this is apparently in vain, because sooner or later a winter comes along with a particularly heavy snowfall. The Carolina wrens starve to death, and they are exterminated back to the southern limits of this heavy snowfall.

So we may forget about laws of temperature control, isothermal lines, and Life-Zones in the sense of latitudinal belts crossing the continent. They are of no real use or biological validity in the great lowlands of eastern North America. I was brought up to believe that the hooded warbler was a Carolinian Zone bird, the golden-winged warbler was a Transition Zone bird, and the Canada warbler a Canadian Zone bird. I can well recall my surprise and perturbation when I found all three species nesting in the same rhododendron swamp in northern New Jersey! It was obvious that their presence there could have nothing whatever to do with any isothermal lines or laws of temperature control.

But Life-Zones have very tangible and definite validity in mountain ranges, especially the lofty ranges in the West, where altitude causes profound difference in rainfall as well as temperature. It has been well said that 100 feet of altitude is roughly equivalent to going north one degree of latitude. Anyone who starts in the hot deserts at the eastern base of the Sierra Nevada of California and ascends to snow line will pass through five distinct Life-Zones, and in each one the vegetation, bird, and mammal life will change abruptly; the rainfall will steadily increase upward. These changes are so obvious as to be readily noticeable to the casual tourist as well as the naturalist. On some of the highest summits of the West there are a few arctic birds. In the Hudsonian Zone just below it one can see the pine grosbeak, three-toed woodpecker, and great gray owl, all breeding at sea level in northern Canada. In the Canadian Zone next below are many of the common birds of the "north woods" at sea level.

These Life-Zones and mountain ranges should be compared with the Andes and their Zones, of which we read in an earlier chapter. While equally obvious and distinct, biologically they are not comparable. A traverse of the Sierra Nevada yields 200 species at most, compared to 1,750, and many of them migrate south in late summer. In North America the whole mountain range is in the Temperate Zone to start with; in the Andes the Temperate Zone is only one out of four. It follows that the Life-Zones of mountain ranges in the north temperate land masses of the world are minor divisions of one Zone only. In the Andes the birds of the Subtropical and Temperate Zones are highly modified birds derived originally from the tropics at their base; only the birds of the Paramo Zone are the same as those at sea level further south. In our western mountains the birds of the upper zones are *not* highly modified birds derived from the climates at their bases. Either most of them breed at sea level at varying distances to the north, or they are migratory species of southern origin, present for a few months only each year.

REFERENCES

1. ALLEN, J. A. Origin and Distribution of North American Birds. *Auk*, 1893, pp. 97–150.
2. MERRIAM, C. HART. Geographic Distribution of Animals and Plants in North America. *Year Book, U. S. Dept. of Agriculture*, 1894, pp. 203–214.
3. MERRIAM, C. HART. Geographic Distribution of Life in North America. *Proceedings of the Biological Society of Washington*, vol. 7, 1892, pp. 1–64.
4. DICE, LEE R. *Biotic Provinces of North America*. Ann Arbor: University of Michigan Press, 1943. 78 pp., 1 map.

    Based primarily on vegetation and major ecological communities. The "biotic province" approximates the "fauna" of Allen. The "life belt" is a vertical subdivision of the "biotic province," and equals the montane Life-Zones of Merriam and other American ornithologists. No division of lowland America into Life-Zones is even hinted at.

5. KENDEIGH, S. CHARLES. A Study of Merriam's Temperature Laws. *Wilson Bulletin*, vol. 44, 1932, pp. 129–143.
6. SHELFORD, VICTOR E. Life Zones, Modern Ecology, and the Failure of Temperature Summing. *Ibid.*, pp. 144–157.
7. DAUBENMIRE, R. F. Merriam's Life-Zones of North America. Quarterly Review of Biology, vol. 13, 1938, pp. 327–332.

    The last three titles attack Merriam's theories, and give references to much earlier criticism.

8. POTZGER, J. E., and THARP, B. C. Pollen Record of Canadian Spruce and Fir from Texas Bog. *Science*, vol. 98, no. 2557, p. 584.

CHAPTER X

CLASSIFICATION AND THE SPECIES CONCEPT

THE classification of living birds, or, for that matter, any other large group of animals, is full of hopeless difficulties and insoluble problems.

The whole purpose of classification stems from a desire of the orderly human mind to have the known facts neatly filed away in a graduated series of pigeonholes in the great desk of Natural History. There are large pigeonholes for the *orders*, such as the ostrich, the herons, the hawks, the parrots, and the songbirds. There are smaller holes for families, in songbirds, crows, swallows, and thrushes. There are still smaller holes for the *genera*, in thrushes, the robin, the bluebird, and true thrushes. Finally there are the fundamental units of classification, the *species*, in the case of the thrushes, the wood, the hermit, and the olive-backed thrushes. These various categories are based on degrees of difference. They begin with specific differences of color and size; genera involve minor structural differences, and families and orders are based on profound or many combinations of profound structural and anatomical characters. In so reasonable a scheme, all would be well if all living birds would only fit into it. Let us be honest, and admit that the evolution of birds has proceeded without the slightest consideration being shown to our desires for a clear-cut and orderly arrangement.

Birds have a long history in geological time, beginning with Archaeopteryx in the Jurassic and the strange toothed birds of the Cretaceous. Modern orders and the principal families go back to Eocene and Miocene time. Living birds can, consequently, be considered from two points of view. Let an imaginary line across the top of the page represent the present. The systematist arranges his living birds along this line, beginning at the left with the most primitive and oldest types. The first twenty-two orders and eighty-three families of birds will appear as a series of well-spaced dots, stretching across two-thirds of the line.

The order of the totipalmate or totally web-footed swimming birds, which includes several distinct families, the pelicans, the cormorants, and the gannets, among others, may be used for example. In North America, there are two species of pelican, the brown pelican and the white pelican. Any tyro who is given a textbook on birds and who is shown some pictures can recognize any member of these families or the two species of pelicans at sight the first time he ever sees them at the range of a quarter of a mile. Trouble begins with the next four orders and seventeen families, which occupy most of the right-hand third of my imaginary line across the page. The number of fundamental differences between these orders and families has decreased, the number of species involved has greatly increased, and there has been some disagreement among authorities as to the exact number of these orders and families.

The last order of modern birds is the order Passeres, the so-called passerine or Songbirds. This order occupies the last right-hand half-inch of our imaginary top line. While the youngest in point of evolution, it is also the dominant group of living birds, and contains more than half the known birds of the world. So many and so crowded are the dots to represent the families in this order that it would require a microscope to separate them in the small space remaining.

If we were consistent in our criteria for family characters, there would be only three possible family groups in passerine birds. Only one-fifth of the species would be in two of these families, leaving at least 5,000 species in one gigantic family. The sixty-five families that are currently recognized are consequently arbitrary divisions, for purposes of practical convenience only, and are not worth further discussion here.

Students of North American birds are familiar with several so-called families peculiar to the New World, now chiefly tropical in distribution. These are the Icteridae (orioles, blackbirds, hang-nests, etc.), the tanagers, the vireos, and the wood warblers. The real facts are that these "families" all merge into each other and into a special New World subfamily of the finches, which includes such familiar birds as the cardinal and rose-breasted grosbeak. Even if we should call them all subfamilies, they would not be strictly homologous to similar groups in earlier orders;

no one, for instance, has any difficulty recognizing an ani, a peculiar subfamily of the cuckoos, or a road runner, still another subfamily of the same family. With a number of tropical American birds there is no way to settle whether they shall be called tanagers or finches.

The second point of view is naturally enough the historical one. All living birds are terminals of genealogical or ancestral lines going back in an unbroken series of generations for millions of years to bird-like reptiles. Our five thrushes, for instance, must be descended from some ancestral thrush. Our bluebirds, robins, and thrushes go back to a common ancestor, a founder of the thrush family, so to speak. This bird, along with the ancestral crows, swallows, finches, and larks, must also, in turn, be descended from a primitive ancestral song, or passerine bird, the prototype of the order. These facts are implied by the whole theory of evolution. The bottom line of the page is, consequently, the Eocene period in early geological time. The reader will imagine a gigantic genealogical tree the main trunk of which goes up the right hand side of the page; all the dots along the top line are the ends of twigs, springing from branches of increasing size, merging into fewer and larger main limbs downwards and those furthest to the left tend to spring from the main trunk furthest down, to show that they branch off first.

It follows that the classification of living birds is at the mercy of an unknown genealogy, as the fossil record is hopelessly fragmentary. It also clearly follows that, in our view of living birds today, the unquestioned distinctness of certain species, families, or orders is solely due to the extinction of all the intermediate types and "missing links," which must once have existed under the premises of evolution. The hopeless chaos of modern passerine birds is due to their recent and rapid evolution and the welter of intermediate types and connecting links, all of which have survived and all of which occur simultaneously on earth. Reasoning by analogy, it will require another million years of evolution before we can hope for a stable and clear-cut classification of this order.

There is, however, a serious fallacy in stressing this imperfect fossil record, which some systematic ornithologists give as the main excuse for the unsatisfactory classification of birds. Let us suppose that we actually came into the possession of a perfect series of fossil specimens, representing *every single* one of the million generations between the wood thrush of today and the ancestor of the Order of perching and songbirds. It is obvious that our proposed system of classification would again become hopeless. We couldn't possibly tell where and how to draw any line between the present-day species and the ancestral species, the ancestral genus, family, and Order, as there would obviously be no break or gap of any kind.

Let us now return to the species, the so-called fundamental unit of systematic classification. What is a species? How do we recognize it as such? And what valid criteria, if any, exist? The answer, to be honest, is that we are still unable to give a final definition. There are no universally valid criteria which are capable of experimental proof. It turns out that there are a good many different kinds or types of species and quite frequently the degree of difference visible to us, what I might call the obvious external characters, are of little importance to the birds. Two birds strikingly different in appearance may be more closely related than two others which are barely distinguishable to us.

In the first place, there is the very helpful modern concept of the superspecies, which is a group of species more closely related to each other than other species in the same genus. An ideal example is furnished in the United States by the warblers. One of the very large warbler genera is the genus Dendroica, which contains a great variety of strikingly distinct species, such as the well-known yellow and myrtle warblers, the black-throated blue and the black-throated green. The black-throated green has several relatives in different parts of the United States. There is the golden-cheeked warbler of central Texas, Townsend's warbler of the northern Rockies, and the hermit warbler of the Pacific coast ranges. All are green, black, gold, and white, and these colors occur in various combinations or percentages. A hybrid between the last two species has recently been described. The immature of all four species are much more nearly alike. This is a frequent happening in songbirds, and suggests a former common ancestor. I might add that all four of these warblers migrate southward to winter in southern Mexico and northern Central America, and it would be possible in the wintertime to find all four species in one flock. All four are clearly more like each other than any other warbler, and furnish an ideal example of what is meant by a superspecies in modern systematic ornithology.

Another example of the superspecies in North American birds is the welter of forms of the genus junco, especially in the western United States. No one can agree as to just how many species of the genus junco there are. In certain cases their ranges overlap. If they are species, they hybridize freely, or, if they are to be regarded as subspecies, there are the usual intergrading or intermediate individuals. Farther south in Central America there are isolated juncos above tree line on the tops of the highest volcanoes. This is a clear case where a superspecies includes all the possible or supposed species; and the superspecies and the genus are one and the same thing. Americans are not so likely to appreciate the fact that our brant and Canada goose really constitute one superspecies in this particular genus (*Branta*) of geese, as they are very much more like each other than they are like the totally different red-breasted goose of Siberia.

There are only two shrikes in North America, the northern shrike and the loggerhead shrike. They are surprisingly alike, different only in certain minor characteristics, especially in size. In Europe there is a precisely similar situation. There is a larger, gray shrike in northern Europe, and there is a small, very similar shrike, known as the lesser gray shrike, in southern Europe. The great gray shrike ranges eastward across Russia and the whole of Siberia to the extreme northeastern sections of Asia. The northern shrike in Alaska is only a subspecies of this shrike in eastern Siberia. There is, consequently, one Holarctic superspecies going around the entire northern hemisphere, which is sharply distinct from a great many Old World shrikes, which are chestnut or red-backed, or have bright yellow under parts and other totally different types of coloration and markings.

Species of birds can be either *sympatric* or *allopatric*. Species of birds are sympatric when they occupy the same area and do not interbreed, no matter how closely they may resemble each other. There are four common and well-known thrushes in eastern North America, all occasionally breeding in the same area. The hermit thrush and veery need no comment, but the gray-cheeked and the olive-backed thrushes are so closely similar that many decades ago one of the leading American ornithologists argued that they were nothing but individual color variations of one species. It was not until they were found to have slightly different breeding ranges, definitely different breeding habits, and totally different songs that American ornithologists became convinced that here were two remarkably close, but really distinct, species of birds.

Another illustration of two sympatric species brings out a slightly different point. The adult male blackpoll and bay-breasted warblers are as different and as distinct as any two North American warblers I can think of, but the young in the first fall plumage are exceedingly similar. The bay-breast differs only in averaging a little more buffy yellow below all the way to the under-tail coverts, whereas the blackpoll warbler is whiter, with white under-tail coverts; the bay-breasted warbler also has blackish legs, and the blackpoll warbler pinkish legs. Here again, the great similarity of the young of these two species of warblers suggests that they originally sprang from a common ancestor. It affords another illustration of how birds which appear to us strikingly distinct may be, in fact, quite closely related. The more we learn about the genetics and inheritance of color characters in birds, the more it begins to appear that striking differences in the color of birds may be due to a very small number of genetic characters.

The bay-breasted and the blackpoll warblers may be compared with two other warblers of the same genus that occur in exactly the same wood together in the breeding season, the magnolia and the Blackburnian. They are completely distinct in every phase of their lives. Consequently, it should be clear that there are degrees of difference between different species of warblers.

Under the heading of sympatric species, or those occupying the same breeding area without interbreeding, we have a remarkable group of species called *sibling* species. These birds are so astonishingly similar in appearance as to be almost indistinguishable at all times of the year. An outstanding example in Europe is the brown creeper. Our familiar brown creeper in North America is the same species of creeper also found in Europe, but there are *two* species in Europe. They differ only in that one has a long claw on the hind toe, which is nearly straight, and the other has a much shorter claw on the hind toe, which is strongly curved, and they have strikingly distinct songs. The matter has been thoroughly tested. The two birds occur together. They never interbreed.

There are several similar cases in New World flycatchers. The small flycatchers of the genus *Empidonax* are famous for giving bird students much trouble; there are many closely related species that are practically indistinguishable as far as size and color differences are concerned, but their songs turn out to be distinct, their eggs may be differently colored, and their habitat preferences are very marked. In the crested flycatchers of the genus *Myiarchus*, I have myself had field experience with a remarkable pair of species in Central America. One is Nutting's flycatcher, which just reaches north into southern Arizona. With it occurs another species which only differs in the fact that it has a slightly shorter tail, and this difference in the tail length is not sufficiently great so that the two birds can be told apart in life. Nevertheless, the careful collecting of specimens in the breeding season, the watching of nests, proves that there are actually two distinct species of these flycatchers, the individuals of which keep apart. In Amazonian Brazil there are other species of *Myiarchus* and *Elainea* that are colored almost exactly alike, but some are larger and others are smaller.

The great South American tropical group of ant-birds provides a series of cases where the males of two species in the same section of forest are indistinguishable, so far as we can discover, and where the females can be separated only by slight differences in the shade of brown, which would ordinarily be regarded as a subspecific character only. All these factors combined lead to the most modern and up-to-date definition of a species, namely, that it consists of actually or potentially interbreeding populations, no matter how different they may seem to be, reproductively isolated from other such groups, no matter how similar they may appear to be.

If the sibling species illustrates one extreme, the jungle fowl of tropical Asia excellently illustrate the other. There are three wild, true species known. The Indian jungle fowl, which is the ancestor of all our domestic breeds of poultry and chickens, has a notched or scalloped comb, the hackles on the sides of the neck and shoulders are bright yellow, the general body coloration of the bird is a shade of dark red, and it has fourteen tail feathers. Another species of jungle fowl, in Burma, is like the Indian jungle fowl in most of these characteristics, but the hackles, instead of being yellow, are barred black and white. In Java, there is a third species of jungle fowl which has sixteen tail feathers, the comb is entire, and the general body coloration is blacker, less yellow and red. As I have already remarked, the Indian jungle fowl is the ancestor of all breeds of domestic poultry, but bantams and the gamecocks are almost identical with the ancestral jungle fowl, which still lives wild in India today. Consider what selection under domestication has done for the jungle fowl. What reader would care to claim that a barred "Plymouth Rock" or an "Andalusian Blue" or a Japanese Black and White Chicken with tail feathers up to twenty-three feet long, was not far more strikingly different from a bantam rooster than is the Burmese Sonnerat's jungle fowl?

It further appears that all domestic breeds of poultry are fertile among themselves, and produce *fertile* offspring when mated with the wild, Indian jungle fowl. It turns out that all three true wild species also hybridize with each other and with domestic poultry, but the hybrids are *not fertile*. These facts afford final experimental proof that very distinct-looking birds to us may, in fact, be identical species, and that two different species of jungle fowl are much more alike in appearance than some of the breeds of domestic poultry.

We have here, in passing, an illustration of what is meant by "reproductive isolation." The three true species of jungle fowl are reproductively isolated in two respects. In the first place, their ranges do not coincide in nature, and consequently they do not interbreed because, geographically speaking, they cannot. But, experimentally, the opportunity is given them to do so, and they are unable to produce fertile offspring, one final test of reproductive isolation.

In sharp contrast to sympatric species, there are *allopatric* species, birds which are closely related apparently, but occupying separate geographic areas. It must be admitted that in a great many cases no clear-cut line can be drawn between them and subspecies, because the test of reproductive isolation is in nature impossible, or has not yet been made by experiment. The four warblers of the black-throated green group, already discussed, afford an excellent illustration. The juncos, as already pointed out, illustrate a very difficult case, which will be finally settled only by large-scale breeding experiments with captive birds. There are many familiar examples where eastern species are "represented" by distinct western species: the eastern and chestnut-backed bluebirds, the rose-breasted and black-headed grosbeaks, indigo and lazuli bunting, myrtle and Audubon's warbler. Probably no one would question the propriety of calling these birds distinct species, though most of them are in the same superspecies.

Complications arise in comparing the eastern and western meadow larks, which would be siblings if they occurred together. The songs are quite distinct, but the only differences of coloration are more white in the outer tail feathers of the western, combined with a reduction in the black bars and borders. Actually the two birds come together in some of the plains and prairie states, but apparently they are perfectly reproductively isolated. It should consequently be clear that there are varying degrees of difference between "representative" species.

Passing to another type of "species," only partial reproductive isolation has been attained. In sympatric species there is the famous example of the two warblers in New England. These two birds, the blue-winged warbler and the golden-winged warbler, are only partially sympatric, in the sense that their breeding ranges overlap for only about one-third; otherwise, the blue-winged warbler is southern and the golden-winged warbler is northern. But where their breeding ranges overlap they hybridize freely and produce fertile offspring, and the point of particular interest about them is that inheritance is of the type popularly called Mendelian. In other words, the characters of one parent, the golden-winged warbler, are "dominant" over those of the "recessive" blue-winged warbler, so that the offspring known as Brewster's warbler in the first generation is much more like a golden-winged warbler than it is like a blue-winged warbler. Once in a great many times, and only in a second generation mating, the very rare and little known Lawrence's warbler is produced, which is obviously more like the blue-winged warbler, but has the wing patch and the black throat and head markings of the golden-winged warbler. These warblers may be profitably contrasted with my earlier illustration of the blackpoll and the bay-breasted, which nest in the same woods over a much more extensive area, but nobody can imagine their trying to interbreed or succeeding in producing fertile offspring.

The eastern golden-shafted and western red-shafted flickers are allopatric species, which meet and interbreed in the Great Plains. One has yellow wing-linings and tail feathers and black moustache stripes; the other has red linings and tail feathers and red moustache stripes. The fertile hybrid is a perfect intermediate; the wing-linings are orange, and the moustache stripe is mixed black and red. Certain hybrid specimens are remarkable in being bilaterally asymmetrical; the moustache stripe is black on one side and red on the other!—a very rare phenomenon in nature.

There is still another way in which bird species may be contrasted, for which there is no ready explanation at hand. There are species which are *monotypic*, which means that they do not break up into subspecies, races, or geographical varieties no matter how wide a range of territory they occupy and no matter how great are the climatic differences in different portions of their range. In one sense they show no response to variations of their environment; their characters appear stable and fixed.

The majority of bird species, however, are *polytypic*, which means that they do vary in response to differences in environment and climate, and consequently they do break up into races, subspecies, or geographical varieties. This is a point which is particularly troublesome to the amateur bird student, and just what the ornithologist means by subspecific variation should be explained.

Theoretically, subspecies differ from species in that there is complete *intergradation* in differences of size or in shade of coloration. Far northern bald eagles, ravens, hairy and downy woodpeckers, are very large; individuals from the southern limits of these species are very small; all intermediate geographical areas are occupied by birds of intermediate size, and there is a *perfect progression* in size as we proceed northward from the smallest to the largest. In this situation it is clearly impossible to call the extremes distinct species. This type of variation is a very different thing from the absolute and striking differences between a rose-breasted and a black-headed grosbeak. Similarly, desert song sparrows are paler and grayer than the eastern song sparrow of a more humid climate, which in turn is smaller and paler than the giant, dark and rusty song sparrows of the very humid coast of Alaska and the Aleutian Islands. At least half the species of passerine birds of North America show some subspecific variation.

Technically, subspecies are formally described and given a scientific name. It is a third name tacked on to the generic and specific names. Thus the hairy woodpecker is called *Dryobates villosus* as a species. The northern hairy is *Dryobates villosus septentrionalis;* the eastern hairy is called *Dryobates villosus villosus*, as the first one described; the southern hairy is named *D. v. auduboni*. In all scientific works and articles the correct subspecific name must be given. Recalling my remarks about size variation in this woodpecker on an earlier page, another technical point is inevitable. The number of subspecies to be named and recognized is entirely a matter of opinion or convenience. There might just as well be ten subspecies as three, all based on average differences of size in ten or three latitudinal belts. No matter which number is named, none can be *identified in life;* all require series of carefully sexed museum specimens, which must be carefully and accurately measured. The same remarks apply to subspecies based on varying shades of color. Five subspecies of the Savannah sparrow winter commonly in Texas; the careful expert can occasionally perceive that some are grayer, some browner, and some blacker, but specimens must be shot and compared with carefully named series in the better museums before the subspecies can be identified. About half the birds listed in the official North American Check-List are sub-species, which the amateur bird student can never hope really to identify in life. This is why he dislikes subspecies, as he has neither the time nor the inclination to shoot and skin specimens.

Actually, however, subspecies are of fundamental bi-ological significance and consequently of great interest. It has been well said that the subspecies of today are the *incipient species* of tomorrow. If the theory of evolution be granted, if we admit that the living species of today are descended from the vanished species of yesterday, we may well ask how this could have come about if the species of the past had had no capacity to vary. If all living birds today were monotypic, and none polytypic, evolution in birds would be over.

The probable or possible course of events can be illustrated in two different directions in living birds. In certain great chains of subspecies the extremes are so different that they are easily distinguished in life, and they would unquestionably be regarded as distinct allopatric species were it not for the intermediates. The only step required is the extinction of these intermediates. Such cases are frequent in tropical archipelagoes, especially in Polynesia and Melanesia, and have been well described by Dr. Ernst Mayr in his book "Systematics and the Origin of Species." Certain northern gulls furnish an even more graphic illustration. Any student of birds can learn to recognize the herring gull and the Iceland gull in our winter harbors, the California gull of the Pacific coast, the les-

Dr. A. A. Allen

IVORY–BILLED WOODPECKER

At nest, Singer Tract, Louisiana. This bird is practically extinct: only three individuals are known to be left alive.

Allan D. Cruickshank

TREE SWALLOWS ON MIGRATION

ser black-backed gull of northern and western Europe, and the yellow-legged herring gull of the Mediterranean. All are members of a great chain of subspecies which go around the world and are completely connected by intermediate subspecies in one section of the world or another. The lesser black-backed gull and herring gull in Europe now occupy in part the same general area, and *nest together* in the same colony. They are perfectly reproductively isolated, and consequently behave in every way like two distinct species, which in this case are sympatric instead of allopatric.

There are other cases, however, where final judgment is a matter of opinion. Students in New England are well acquainted with the common Savannah sparrow and its large pale relative, the Ipswich sparrow, which breeds only on Sable Island, Nova Scotia, and winters in the sand dunes of the Atlantic seaboard. Until very recently the Ipswich sparrow was regarded as a distinct species on the following counts: (1) the differences were absolute and easily recognizable in life; (2) there can be no geographic intermediates between mainland and island populations. The Savannah sparrow ranges over the whole continent of North America, however, and it has recently been pointed out that a subspecies in the Aleutian Islands is just as large as the Ipswich sparrow, and other subspecies in Lower California are just as pale. On this argument the Ipswich sparrow is merely one terminal of a great chain of subspecies.

Still another type of variation is illustrated by the long-tailed blue magpie, a remarkable case of discontinuous distribution. One subspecies is confined to Spain, the only other one is in eastern Siberia many thousands of miles away. The differences between them are very slight variations in color and size. If the argument in this chapter has been followed, the reader will see the need for experimental work with captive sparrows and magpies to determine whether they will interbreed and produce fertile offspring or whether they are reproductively isolated. There is an almost endless amount of experimental work of this sort to be done as part of the research of the future. But, when all is said and done, the hopes of the scientist for a "cut and dried" system in nature are doomed to disappointment. The differences between some subspecies will appear more obvious than the differences between some species, and there are enough variable birds in the world so that every conceivable type of intermediate case can be found.

Actually there are even finer divisions in nature than subspecies. Many biological "races," with real genetic characters which are inherited, are absolutely indistinguishable in museum specimens. Most of the really fine modern work in this direction has been done with invertebrates. A recent monograph of the malarial mosquitoes of Europe recognizes six species and various subspecies. The only visible characters are in the larvae; all the others are based on life-history studies of living individuals. The species prove to differ by their inability to hybridize, whether they are carriers of malaria or not, their tolerance to sea water, feeding habits, swarming habits, habitat preferences, and geographic ranges.

In this respect ornithology lags well behind kindred sciences. In North American birds we have just begun to scratch the surface. We are just beginning to recognize that some of our birds are divided into sharply distinct "populations," for lack of a better term. One population of tree swallows has a more northerly winter range on our coastal salt marshes, and survives the regular freezes by eating bayberries; it migrates northward early, and tends to nest near the coast. Another "population" migrates much later, winters farther south, is completely dependent on insect food, and perishes in the rare big "freezes." The myrtle warbler has two "populations" along the same lines. One winters abundantly on Cape Cod, subsisting on bayberries; it does not arrive until mid-November, when the last "inland population" myrtles depart southward; it leaves Cape Cod north-bound in mid-April just as the first "inland" myrtles arrive from the south. Long-continued observation of the most careful kind backed with extensive banding will be required before many such guesses become proved scientific facts. A whole book can be written on the existence of suspected "populations" in many of our commonest birds, the loon, herring gull, common tern, black duck, lesser scaup, blue jay, and brown thrasher, to cite only a few.

As a fundamental biological fact, the great majority of bird species on earth are composed of thousands of "characters," all of which are inherited. It makes no difference in the evolution of the species whether they can be seen in living birds, in museum specimens, or not. It makes no difference how recessive the majority of them may be, or surely are. In the case of domestic poultry, as compared to the wild jungle fowl of India, it is obvious that many thousand generations of selective breeding were required to bring up to the "surface," so to speak, some of the many recessive characters which the jungle fowl actually possessed. To sum up, then, we are still unable to give a final definition of a species, and there are no universally valid criteria, capable of experimental proof. The reason is not the incompetence of the biologist, but the fact that there is nothing final about the species. It evolved only yesterday in geologic time; it will be extinct or greatly changed tomorrow. No two bird species ever originated at the same moment, ever had the same latent capacity to vary, or were ever subjected to exactly the same environmental stresses for the same length of time. If they had, they would be identical, instead of distinct. It follows that the factors causing the evolution of any species of bird cannot be the same in any two cases. Diversity, not uniformity, characterizes the class of birds. How, then, can there be uniform criteria for classification?

REFERENCE

1. MAYR, ERNST. Systematics and the Origin of Species. New York: Columbia University Press, 1942. 8vo, x + 334 pp.
   Technical, and difficult reading for the layman, but the only work in English giving a clear picture of the modern species concept, and the categories below the species.

INDEX